While the Earth Endures

Endures

Creation
Cosmology
and
Climate Change

~~~~

Philip Foster

ISBN 978 1 901546 31 6

Acknowledgements

Extracts from the Authorised Version of the Bible (The King James Bible), the rights in which are vested in the Crown, are reproduced by permission of the Crown's patentee, Cambridge University Press.

Extracts from the NEW AMERICAN STANDARD BIBLE,
© 1960, 1962, 1963, 1968, 1971, 1972, 1973, 1975, 1977, 1995,
By the Lockman Foundation. Used by permission.

Scripture quotations taken from the HOLY BIBLE,
NEW INTERNATIONAL VERSION
copyright © 1973, 1978, 1984 by International Bible Society
Used by permission of Hodder & Stoughton,
a division of Hodder Headline Ltd.
All rights reserved.
"NIV" is a registered trademark of International Bible Society.
UK trademark number 1448790

Front cover: barred spiral galaxy NGC1300B (Hubble 2005_01)

St. Matthew Publishing Ltd
1 Barnfield, Common Lane, Hemingford Abbots
Huntingdon PE28 9AX   UK
01480 399098
Email: PF.SMP@dial.pipex.com
www.stmatthewpublishing.co.uk

While the Earth

Endures

Contents

List of diagrams and pictures

To the many scientists and others who, while patiently investigating the causes and consequences of climate variation, have had to endure public obloquy and personal abuse from the Pharisees of a new religious Inquisition.

Rulers persecute me without cause,
but my heart trembles at your word.
Ps 119:161

Foreword

Please read this book. It is an amazing work of intricate scholarship covering two of the world's most vexed questions. Where is God and whose side is 'she' or he on?

As you can see from this statement I am no theologian but an academic botanist who likes to think that he is of the same ilk as those vicars who served their flock wisely whilst also laying the foundations of Natural History.

The first half of this labour of the love of God looks at the pros and cons of creation and evolution by natural selection.

My own considered opinion is that because of the configuration of the make up of the very elements that constitute every scrap of the universe, a process I like to call creative evolution, it just *had to* happen.

It doesn't matter if God pushed the 'Big Bang' button seven days or seven billion years ago. It was pushed and we are either blessed or burdened by the presence of the creative power within.

The other half of this primer of atmospheric science pertains to the action of the so called 'greenhouse gases'.

The author's knowledge and understanding of both sides of this highly topical argument are amazing and are set out in easily understood language.

We both are of the same opinion that so-called 'global warming' is not man made but a natural phenomenon.

Why so many people have followed the devils of greed and avarice in this matter we find hard to understand, especially when many supposedly follow Christian beliefs.

However, in the simplest of terms, if global warming is man made then the insurance companies will make a killing; if it is a natural phenomenon, we cannot sue God!

David Bellamy
Bedburn, December 2008

While the earth endures,
Seedtime and harvest,
And cold and heat,
And summer and winter,
And day and night
Shall not cease.
Genesis 8:22

Preface to the Second Edition

It was Owl who explained to Pooh that the opposite of an Introduction was a Contradiction[†]. There is an element of this in the second edition. Scientific knowledge moves on, making knew discoveries and, as in this instance, also rediscovering overlooked material from the past.

When I first wrote my book I still held the view that there was a 'greenhouse effect' due to greenhouse gases in the atmosphere. I took that view because, when I did physics, I was taught that a greenhouse was a radiation trap. That is also what I taught my students. But *'Nullius in Verba'* - on the word of no one - it turns out that this is mistaken. A hundred years ago a simple, but elegant, experiment demonstrated unequivocally that this theory is quite wrong. The details of this are included in Appendix 1 and the text on the greenhouse effect has been rewritten.

In November 2009 the 'Climategate' leak hit the headlines. This will be examined briefly in Appendix 2. Sufficient to say here that the emails merely confirmed what most realists had long sensed - that the public was being deliberately misled over a supposed man-made climate crisis. The subsequent whitewash of the University of East Anglia by Lord Oxburgh was a shameful piece of further fraud. Lord Oxburgh, who headed the "investigation", happens to make his millions from building wind turbines. Lord Oxburgh is chairman of Falck Renewables, a manufacturer of windfarms and the UK subsidiary of The Falck Group, a Milan-based manufacturer. A sister company of Oxburgh's Falck Renewables, Actelios, is publicly traded and had suffered serious falls in its stock price during the period of Climategate. Lord Oxburgh's company, its parent and more than one of its sister companies have had organised crime activities surrounding their acquisition of property and installation of green energy systems.

Oxburgh is also director of Globe International a lobby group that pushes the case that global warming is a real threat. It is being funded by the taxpayer and assisted by the BBC. The little-known, not-for-profit firm works behind the scenes at international conferences to further its aims. Allied to this group is the Grantham Institute, another pressure

[†]*The House at Pooh Corner,* A.A.Milne.

group funded by Jeremy Grantham a multi-billionaire 'green' investment specialist. Its director is Prof. Sir Brian Hoskins, another promoter of alarmism.*

With the arrival of a coalition government in the UK, we face further absurdities 'fighting' climate change, with huge costs to the taxpayer, yet we seem to be living in the 'Dead Parrot Sketch' from *Monty Python*. Most intelligent people are highly sceptical of the assertions of the scaremongers, but find it difficult to inject any sanity into the situation. But there are politicians who will take a principled stand, chief among whom I would name as Sammy Wilson of the DUP who lost his ministerial job at Stormont by standing up for the truth: he refused to allow the showing of a UK government propaganda advert about man-made climate change. MPs such as Graham Stringer, Peter Lilley, Andrew Tyrie and David Davis have spoken out on the issue as, of course, has Lord Lawson. Among MEPs I would commend Roger Helmer and Geoffrey Bloom. I know there are many others who are fighting hard and all require our prayers.

*http://www.telegraph.co.uk/earth/environment/climatechange/8469883/Lobby ists-who-cleared-Climategate-academics-funded-by-taxpayers-and-the-BBC.html

Introduction

The first to present his case seems right,
till another comes forward and questions him.   Prov 18:17

The year 2009 marks four relevant anniversaries: 400 years since Galileo first turned his telescope to the heavens, 200 years since the birth of Charles Darwin, 150 years since the publication of *On the Origin of Species* and 50 years since Bert Bolin put forward the hypothesis that man-made carbon dioxide was heating the planet.

This book may well cause upset. In it I try to tackle a range of issues that sometimes divide Christians (and others) about the nature of God's Creation.

Part I, which deals with the arguments for and against Recent Creationism, may be irrelevant for some readers and they may want to skip on to Part II.

I am writing as a creationist: of what sort the book will reveal. I find that neo-Darwinism and its variations are, as theories, scientifically poorly attested. Much, if not all, of the supporting evidence is ambivalent at best. As Mark Twain observed, "There is something fascinating about science. One gets such wholesale returns of conjecture out of such a trifling investment of fact." Continental biologists, for example, do not view Darwin with the near god-like status he seems to have acquired in the Anglo-Saxon world and Biochemistry has left neo-Darwinism with nothing to say.

My own qualifications are that I have degrees in Natural Science (Biochemistry) and in Theology, both from Cambridge. I taught Physics and Chemistry to A level in Nigeria and since then have spent nearly thirty years in active church ministry. I have always maintained my interest in the sciences and in the relationship of science to the Scriptures. I have also had an interest in the tendency we all seem to have, be we Christian or otherwise, of being deluded. My interest in climate science and the activism some of it has inspired, along with its rapid elevation to religious status, has been more recent.

The debate over the reality of human-induced global warming is steeped in emotion and hysteria: I gave a talk to a Christian group near Oxford in 2008 on the issue. When the programme was sent out, the chaplain of an Oxford college (which, to save the college from embarrassment, I will not name) was urging people *not* to go to the talk. I have to say that the meeting was, nonetheless, quite well attended.

Even as I write it is beginning to look as if the wheels may be coming off the Global Warming/Climate Change band-wagon: I may seem to be acting like Tom Lehrer, who remarked about some of his satirical songs, "I like to take the various forms of the popular song and 'kick them when they're down'."

The Bible has an excellent test for prophets in Deut. 18:21-22:

You may say to yourselves, "How can we know when a message has not been spoken by the LORD?"

If what a prophet proclaims in the name of the LORD does not take place or come true, that is a message the LORD has not spoken. That prophet has spoken presumptuously. Do not be afraid of him.

The prophets of man-made Climate Change/Global Warming have a remarkable record for their predictions, of which they have made plenty—100% failure to date.

Let me make it clear that I believe we are called to look after the world God has given us and that we should not be wasteful or profligate with resources, but also we should be generous in our giving. But it is both pointless and dishonest to promote untruthful reasons for doing any of these things. It will lead to a severe backlash as people discover that they have been deceived.

Let me also make it clear, as others have had to do when writing about this area, that I have never received any money from the energy industry in any way. The research for this book has been done without any financial support from any special interest group. It is ridiculous to have to write these things, but unfortunately too much of this debate is conducted *ad hominem*.

I have not included multiple references. Too many would upset the general tone of the book which I have tried to make as accessible

2

as possible. I have put some notes and details in grey boxes. Some of these may be a little technical and all can be passed over without losing the general sense of the argument. Today with the Internet it does not take too long to check out the details of any assertions, as long as discernment is used. Trying to be accessible brings with it dangers of over-simplifying some of the issues or some of the science. It is inevitable that I have sometimes had to do this.*

* It is unfortunate that standards of science teaching, even at sixth form level, are patchy, particularly in such areas as 'environmental science'.

One student I know, on their first day at an environmental science class at sixth form, was faced with a teacher who demanded that students who accepted that man-made global warming was true were to stand in one group, but those who did not believe it were to stand in another. It was clear that this was to ensure any sceptics were known about and therefore could be 'worked on'. That is not education but indoctrination.

Thanks are due to many people for their help in this book.

Foremost, to my long-suffering wife, Cordelia, who has endured months (even years) of my discussing and arguing with friends and visitors and has never once complained, but has been incredibly supportive throughout.

To Dr. Philip Dean who first started me off on this interesting journey.

To June Manwell, along with others, who read through the draft and made vital suggestions and corrections.

My thanks go to many people who have forwarded to me scientific papers, articles etc. about the issues in the book.

To Dr Colin Merritt for help and information.

To David Bellamy who graciously agreed to write the foreword.

None of the above is responsible for any errors or opinions expressed herein.

If there is any value in this book then the glory must go to God, who is the Creator, Sustainer and the Redeemer of the world through his Son Jesus Christ, in whom all things hold together (Col 1:17).

Philip Foster
December 2008

A note about units and measurements

In this book I have used a mixture of measurement units. In general, where we are dealing with specifically scientific matters, I have stuck with SI (Système International) metric units, but when addressing more general ideas I sometimes have used Imperial measurements, eg m.p.h., miles per second or gallons.

Strictly speaking a unit has no plural. The unit is a *quality* not a *quantity*. The number *before* the unit is the quantity, the unit itself is what kind of measurement it is.

In the SI system there are three fundamental units, **Mass**, kilogram (kg); **Length**, metre (m); **Time**, second (s). All other units are derived from these three.

Thus in science we write of a distance of 100 *metre* (abbreviated '*m*') not 100 *metres*—which might get abbreviated to '*ms*', which in turn might be mistaken for *metre second*. Area is in *square metre*, written as *10 m²* etc.

If we want to express speed or velocity it is in *metre per second*. This is usually written as *100 ms⁻¹*. The *s⁻¹* expresses the '*per* second' part. If we want to express acceleration (change of velocity *per* second or change of distance *per* second *per* second) we would write *50 ms⁻²*, the *s⁻²* expressing '*per* second *per* second'.

If this is as clear as mud, try not to worry too much about it!

Other (sometimes confusing) quantities

I use the (now more common) *short scale* throughout:

1 billion = 1000 million, 10^9 (1,000,000,000)

1 gigaton = 1 billion Imperial ton, 1 billion metric tonne or

1000 billion (a trillion) kilogram, 10^{12} kg

(The Imperial ton happens to be very nearly the same as the metric tonne. There are about 2.204 lb to 1 kg and 1000 kg to 1 tonne which equals 2204 lb, whereas the Imperial ton is 2240 lb—now isn't that interesting?)

Where text is quoted from American literature (including the NASB), American spellings are retained. Thus 'vapor' not vapour, 'sulfate' not sulphate etc.

Bjørn Lomborg's book title, *the skeptical environmentalist*, is correctly spelt.

Part I
Creation

Chapter 1

Before we start

What we are going to try and do

First and foremost I intend to preserve the integrity of the Word of God. But I am also going to depart from the current evangelical Christian consensus about the nature of the revelation given in the first chapters of Genesis.

The relatively recent consensus, that Genesis chapters 1-2 describe the creation of the Universe about 6000 years ago and that all scientific data must conform to this premise, has itself a fairly short history. It goes back only to the 1960s when Whitcombe and Morris published one of the first 'creation science' books, *The Genesis Flood*. Before that nearly all evangelical Bible believing Christians were ancient creationists, with just a few being Theistic evolutionists.

This book will try to go back to first principles. No-one is free from prejudice or bias, the author included, but I want us to try and be as objective as possible about what lies before us.

We live in an amazing Universe and we serve an amazing God who sent his Son to die for us that we might be saved from eternal judgement and given eternal life. He gave us his written Word, the Bible, inspired by his Holy Spirit. But it is a book that needs to be rightly handled. We can do damage to the gospel if we interpret the Bible wrongly. Let the offence we cause be the offence of the Cross.

The themes we are going to tackle are huge: they don't come much bigger than Creation, Cosmology and Climate Change, but I hope that by the end we shall be amazed at the awesomeness of the God and Father of our Lord Jesus Christ.

How do science and Scripture relate where they overlap in reference to the natural world?

Do we use the Bible to interpret natural phenomena, or let the observations of scientific knowledge help us interpret those parts of the Bible that are concerned with such things?

Let me pose another question. When the Bible predicts *future* events, how do we interpret these? We might look at other parts of Scripture, such as those that predicted the coming of Jesus, to see how they were fulfilled. But the canon of Scripture is now closed (effectively just before AD70—that was when the book of Revelation was completed). Jesus predicted that Jerusalem would fall to the Romans, but nowhere in Scripture are we told that this event took place. Where do we look for its fulfilment? We look in secular history. The Roman and Jewish accounts of that disaster are there for us to read today. We use *secular* historical records to interpret the prophecies of these events. We continue to do that up to the present as we see events unfolding in the world which point us to prophecies in the Bible about times of the End. These historical events themselves, recorded by unbelieving historians, nonetheless help us understand what God inspired the prophets to write. So too, as we shall see, we can use secular science to understand 'retrospective prophecy'—that is, God's revelation in Genesis about the past *before* humans were there.

Chapter 2

Progressive revelation

Scripture operates under this principle: God progressively reveals his purposes. Thus the plan of redemption is first spelt out in Genesis Ch.3, but only in the briefest outline. Then more and more of the detail is filled out in the Old Testament until we see the full revelation becoming reality in the New Testament as "The Word became flesh and dwelt among us" [see Fruchtenbaum's *Messianic Christology*]. Then, in the New Testament, prophecy about the Second Coming is progressively revealed; first Jesus' Olivet discourse, the epistles of Paul and Peter ending with the Book of Revelation being the final and most detailed (and perhaps also most cryptic) exposition of these future events.

How is this important for understanding the Bible's accounts of creation and natural phenomena?

Genesis is one of the five books of the prophet Moses. The description of Creation in Genesis was in some way revealed to Moses.

We can reasonably state that Moses was not present as the events of creation unfolded. No one was, except God the Trinity.

"Where were you when I laid the earth's foundation?
Tell me, if you understand."   Job 38:4

So it was revealed to Moses in some way, just as future events were also revealed to him—and to the other prophets of Scripture.

Genesis 1-3 is of the nature of retrospective prophecy—revealing the unknown *past* to man, just as normal prophecy reveals aspects of the *future* to man.

Just as we can use secular history and the discoveries of archaeology to understand the prophecies given in the Bible about the future, we can reasonably use the secular sciences to help us understand aspects of the Genesis account.

Is the Genesis account a definitive description of the full process of God's Creation?

There are some unique features about Genesis Ch.1. It is not in Hebrew poetic form, except for verse 27:

So God created man
in his own image,
in the image of God
he created him;
male and female
he created them.

But nonetheless there is a pattern in the whole progression:

Day One	"Let there be light"	**Day Four**	Let there be lights
Day Two	Sky and waters	**Day Five**	Birds and fishes
Day Three	Land & plants appear	**Day Six**	Land creatures & man

Day Seven
God rests and blesses the Sabbath for mankind.
It is also mankind's first day.

Which brings us to another feature of the account. Each day ends with the refrain, "there was evening and there was morning the xth day."

Notice the order here: evening and morning. The Jewish day starts at sundown when people go to rest and then rise to work in the morning. There is an immediate spiritual message in this: God's pattern for humanity is not work earning rest, but the gift of rest to enable us to work: first the grace of God that we might do the works of God—as Paul tells us in Ephesians 2:8-10,

For it is by grace you have been saved, through faith—and this not from yourselves, it is the gift of God—not by works, so that no-one can boast. For we are God's workmanship, created in Christ Jesus to do good works, which God prepared in advance for us to do.

This lesson is reinforced in the pattern of the whole week: man is created on the sixth day and his first day is the Sabbath. Again, first man rests, then he goes out to do God's work.

8

Then another interesting feature: the first six days are closed off with the refrain, '...evening and morning...', but not the Seventh day. That day is not 'signed off'. We are still in some sense in the Seventh Day, and as the writer to the Hebrews (probably Barnabas) puts it in Heb 4:4-11:

4 For somewhere he has spoken about the seventh day in these words: "And on the seventh day God rested from all his work."

5 And again in the passage above he says, "They shall never enter my rest."

6 It still remains that some will enter that rest, and those who formerly had the gospel preached to them did not go in, because of their disobedience.

7 Therefore God again set a certain day, calling it Today, when a long time later he spoke through David, as was said before:
"Today, if you hear his voice, do not harden your hearts."

8 For if Joshua had given them rest, God would not have spoken later about another day.

9 There remains, then, a Sabbath-rest for the people of God;

10 for anyone who enters God's rest also rests from his own work, just as God did from his.

11 Let us, therefore, make every effort to enter that rest, so that no-one will fall by following their example of disobedience.

Genesis tells us that God rested after he had finished creation, but Scripture also tells us that God is working still. For God to rest does not mean he sits back and does nothing.

16 So, because Jesus was doing these things on the Sabbath, the Jews [Judeans] *persecuted him.*

17 Jesus said to them, "My Father is always at his work to this very day, and I, too, am working."

18 For this reason the Jews tried all the harder to kill him; not only was he breaking the Sabbath, but he was even calling God his own Father, making himself equal with God.

Jn 5:16-18

So God still works, but now this is the work of redemption, or of re-creation.

The prime and central purpose of Genesis 1-3 is spiritual not physical.

This is reinforced by the prologue of John's Gospel. Starting with the same 'in the beginning', the same themes reappear concerning the *Logos*, The Word who creates; there is light and darkness; there is the moon and the sun (John the Baptist and Jesus) and throughout the focus is on redemption and the new birth.

But is Genesis Ch. 1-3 intended to be taken literally? Immediately I pose this question, we become suspicious! Let me rephrase the question.

Is Genesis 1-3 intended as a detailed and precise description of the physical creation of the Cosmos and the earth?

If it is, it is remarkably brief. Many cultures around little Israel had elaborate creation myths: long and often very tedious stories about warring gods and monsters. Genesis is an extraordinary contrast: it is clear, concise and rational.

Remember that Moses was writing for a pre-scientific age. The telescope, the microscope, the spectrograph, the NMR machine and the theories of Copernicus, Kepler, Newton, Faraday, Thompson, Maxwell, Einstein, Bohr, Schrödinger, Hawking etc. were three thousand years plus in the future. If God had revealed to Moses equations like:

$$\frac{\partial^2 \psi}{\partial x^2} + \frac{\partial^2 \psi}{\partial y^2} + \frac{\partial^2 \psi}{\partial z^2} + \frac{8\pi^2 m}{h^2}\left(E + \frac{e^2}{r}\right)\psi = 0$$

$$E = mc^2$$

$$\Delta G = \Delta H - T\Delta S$$

then you can imagine the looks of blank puzzlement on the faces of the people of Israel—perhaps on ours also!

So the revelation of Creation could not be in the language of modern science. Nor was it intended to be, as its prime purpose was spiritual: to make it clear that it is God the Trinity who is the creator of everything that is.

All three persons appear in the first three verses:

1 In the beginning **God** (*elohim* in Hebrew, which is plural) *created the heavens and the earth.*

*2 Now the earth was formless and empty, darkness was over the surface of the deep, and the **Spirit** (ruach in Hebrew) of God was hovering over the waters.*

*3 And God **said** (the Word of God—Jesus), "Let there be light," and there was light.*

Let us look a little more closely at these three verses. It is clear that v.1 is what we might call a heading or title about what is to follow. Note, in passing, that the heavens are created before the earth—a point we shall return to later on as we deal with the individual Days of creation.

In v.2 the subject of the earth (ha aretz) is introduced with a strange use of words: 'formless' and 'empty' or 'void'. Scholars differ as to what this means exactly, but I would suggest the following. Moses is saying to the Israelites, "The earth (that we all know about) did not exist at that time: it just wasn't there." This might seem a trivial statement, but not to ancient peoples. The existence of the earth all around them was a much stronger 'given' than it is to us who are aware of the vastness of space and our place in the physical universe. "When God began to create, the earth was not there at all."

And as the headline 'heavens and the earth' suggest, neither was the earth the first thing God made.

The brooding Spirit of God hovers over the 'waters' and 'the deep'. But does this not suggest that oceans existed in some way?

I think not. Hebrew is a very materialistic language. Its vocabulary is about material things: water, wind, earth, blood, flesh, etc., and at this point in Creation none of these things existed. In fact, nothing material existed at all. Yet words had to be found to express this 'not yet existing' state of, well, nothingness being prepared by the Spirit of God. Thus 'the deep', 'the waters' here are words used as pictures for what I might describe as a 'pregnant emptiness' from which Creation will come forth. Even later on in the Bible waters often represented a state of flux and even chaos—the seas roaring often again a picture for the rebellious nations.

One interpretative translation of 'Now the earth was formless and empty' is, 'Now the earth *became* formless and empty'. This has been taken to suggest a previous creation which in some way was wiped out or built over: this is sometimes called the Gap Theory. I have to say that though such an interpretation of the Hebrew is of course possible, this seems a strange idea. That the account of Creation which is so stately and concise should throw up the possibility of a mysterious pre-existing creation being wiped out without any further reference to it anywhere else in Scripture is certainly odd.

And God said, "Let there be **Light** *."*

And, in the manner of serial plays on TV, I am going to break off here.

Before we can go further with the physical meaning of Genesis Ch.1 we must make a considerable detour starting with a question.

Chapter 3

What are Christians frightened of
in scientific knowledge?

Christians often approach the sciences very defensively, maybe fearful that something in science may undermine their faith. This is a pity. Reference is sometimes made to Paul telling Timothy,

*"O Timothy, keep that which is committed to thy trust, avoiding profane and vain babblings, and oppositions of **science** falsely so called:"*

1 Tim 6:20 KJV

While it might be tempting to see this as a condemnation of modern science, it is not so. Paul uses the Greek word *'gnosis'* for the false spirituality of the mystics and gnostics, not for straightforward investigative science we mean today.

There is one other reference to science in the KJV, in Dan Ch.1:4.

*Children in whom was no blemish, but of good appearance, and skilful in all wisdom, and possessing knowledge, and understanding **science**, and such as had ability in them to stand in the king's palace, and whom they might teach the learning and the language of the Chaldeans.*

This time the word is not 'gnosis' but 'prudence' in the Septuagint (abbreviated to LXX; a Greek translation of the Old Testament). Again this is not referring to modern usage of the word science.

Scientists are sinners of course and are quite able to try and adjust results and ideas to suit their underlying philosophies (their 'gnosis' if you like), but strangely, this very sinfulness acts also as a check to many serious errors in science and a spur towards a better understanding of the physical world.

Scientific endeavours operate in a kind of 'free market'; not financially, but in terms of promoting ideas. It is a highly competitive and public arena. One scientist's idea will be critically and sceptically examined by others in the field to find errors and mistakes—and rightly so. When found there will be no holding back the publishing of the findings! Every scientist wants his work to be accepted as right, so the competitive spirit is very strong and very public.

So in general a wrong-headed idea will rapidly be exposed and replaced with something more likely to be correct. This is however a generality.

If we think about free market economies, how do they work? A new product is produced and sells, then someone else devises a better (or cheaper) version of the product and competition begins. In an ideal market, the better product should win, but of course this does not always happen. Sometimes the old, rather poor grade products win out by establishing a monopoly—by aggressively undercutting or buying out the rival product (eg a large software company bought out and employed rival companies' software engineers just to keep the rivals out of the market). Thus cartels can come into existence. In science too flaky theories become entrenched as if they were monopolies—no-one is prepared to go out on a limb because their research grants are determined by companies or by governments. An example of this is the theory of Evolution. It operates like a cartel, making it almost impossible for any alternative theory to get a hearing. When this happens science loses its way until the cartel falls apart—for whatever reason. Another much more recent example of a cartel is the hypothesis of man-made climate change. It too operates as a monopoly; dissent is not allowed and sceptics are treated like heretics.

An earlier example in the history of science was Copernicus' theory of the solar system. This idea found great difficulty in becoming accepted because the establishment, for a mixture of reasons both scientific and theological, resisted it very strongly. And before you accuse the Church of Rome of blindness in this matter, be aware that Luther agreed with them. He remarked,

> "People gave ear to an upstart astrologer who strove to show that the Earth revolves, not the heavens or the firmament, the sun and the moon... This fool Copernicus wishes to reverse the entire science of astronomy; but sacred Scripture tells us that Joshua commanded the sun to stand still and not the earth."

Scientific knowledge may have to reinterpret our understanding of Scripture in certain areas, as is the case with Copernicus and Galileo. Observation using the telescope presented new knowledge about the solar system which did indeed "reverse the entire science of astronomy". Scientific knowledge often proceeds by a series of revolutions in understanding. It is always provisional; it never should be dogmatic; always sceptical. But Scripture itself is unchanging.

Now for some vocabulary used in science.

Hypothesis

This is the name given in science to someone's hunch or idea to explain some phenomenon or how something works. It is untested and is as likely to be wrong as right! The next step is for experiments and observations to be made to see if they bear out the idea, and, most importantly, experiments done that could contradict the idea. This is part of rigorous science; otherwise the human tendency is only to collect data that support the idea—we all like to be right! But a good scientist will try as hard to disprove his idea as to prove it.

Theory

This word is often confused with hypothesis in ordinary English, but in science a theory only really exists if a hypothesis has been demonstrated to be viable by experiments and observations. In other words, a hypothesis can become a theory if the evidence warrants it. But even so a theory is not 'true' in the absolute sense, because as more scientific knowledge becomes available it may be shown to be wrong, or be in need of serious modification. A theory is always provisional, never absolute. Theories often come and go, but the scientific knowledge or data which they were designed to explain usually does not. Of course, scientific data may be found to be inaccurate or even mistaken due to the human errors of experimenters.*

* For example, in the 1930s, spinach was analysed for its iron content and the laboratory reported that it contained ten times as much iron as other

green leaf vegetables. Thus began a huge campaign to feed children in particular as much spinach as possible (remember *Popeye?*) because it was 'so good for them'. Years later it was discovered that the lab had made a simple calculation error—by a factor of ten. Spinach contains about the same iron content as other greens. Much misery in the nursery and at school could have been avoided if that error had not been made!

Thus Darwin's hypothesis of Evolution, put forward in *On the Origin of Species*, was his idea to explain the Succession of species in the fossil record—how life developed from the 'simple' to the very complex. Some evidence, at least at first, seemed to support the idea, so it gravitated towards being a theory. It remains a theory which has suffered several re-writes as evidence kept cropping up which derailed the original hypothesis. It survives more than anything because no-one in science has produced a better theory. Today, even to non-Christian scientists, it has become very dog-eared, creaking at the seams, as evidence from the biochemistry of life presents it with new and insurmountable hurdles—it may not have long to live.

Anyway, Darwin's Theory has a considerable drawback which makes it questionable if it ever was a rigorous scientific theory rather than a metaphysical one. It lacks two fundamental requirements of a scientific theory. *Repeatability*: you cannot do a laboratory rerun of Evolution to see if it happens; and *falsifiability*: Darwin hedged his theory round with such hurdles so as to make it almost impossible to disprove. Now it must be stated that these drawbacks apply to some other theories as well, particularly those that are about origins, such as the 'Big Bang' Theory or the Creationist Young Earth Theory. All inevitably have similar elements of the metaphysical rather than the true scientific reasoning. This does not necessarily mean they are wrong, but it does mean they cannot be given the status that, for example, Evolution is too often given, of being a settled fact. It can never be that. It is the metaphysical base of Darwin's theory that is its Achilles' heel.

Law

A scientific Law is not usually an explanation of anything but a way of generalising observations.

For example, there are the three laws of motion that Newton proposed or the Law of Gravity or the Laws of Thermodynamics and so on. Newton observed (so it is said) an apple fall to the ground in the orchard at Woolsthorpe Rectory and from that particular observation generalised it into the Law of Gravity affecting everything in the Universe.*

* Two masses, m_1 and m_2 at a distance apart r, attract each other with a force F (called gravity) according to the mathematical relationship:

$$F = \frac{Gm_1m_2}{r^2}$$

Where G is the universal gravitational constant determined experimentally. [$G = 6.672 \times 10^{-11}$ m^3 kg^{-1} s^{-2}]

Notice that Newton's Law of Gravity explains only how gravity behaves: but it does not explain what gravity actually *is*. This remained one of the great and fascinating mysteries of science.

Laws may in due time be modified. Thus, for example, the Laws of Motion are true over a wide range of circumstances, but do not operate correctly at the initial conditions of the Big Bang, in black holes nor in the strange world of subatomic particles (quantum physics).

Fairly early on in the renaissance of thought, scientific knowledge came to a crossroads: Newton versus Descartes.

Newton and Descartes both believed in the power of mathematics to explain the natural world, but how they used that mathematical power was crucially different. Newton basically set out the path of experiment, observation and inferences (or deductions) processed by mathematics. Descartes, following ancient Greek philosophy, believed in imagination and mathematics. Newton got his hands dirty with experiments to find out what *is*. Descartes philosophised and imagined what *might be* and then sought to justify that with mathematics. If the maths worked then the imagined picture was true. Put it another way. You start by imagining how you think things are and use mathematics to justify this. What observations you may make are simply used to illustrate the imagined model.

Newtonian science proceeds by experiments, observations and inferences, then these are modelled using mathematics. But the observations drive the maths.

Things have not changed a great deal. With the advent of the computer, Descartes is back in fashion! Too much 'science' today is done on computers, not in the experimental laboratory or out in the real world. Thus much 'climate science' today is Cartesian (adjective from Descartes) not Newtonian: some researchers are glued to their computers, seldom, if ever, out in the real world, seeing how the real world of climate actually behaves. The result is pretty disastrous for science. The imaginary world of computer models rules over the real world of facts and observations.

This leads me to something in the Christian's own back yard which also takes on the appearance of a monopoly and falls into the Cartesian way of thinking: I refer to Creation Science. Here, it seems to me, we, as Christians, are making much the same mistake as the world can make in science. I believe it to be bad for proper scientific enquiry and ultimately unhelpful for our Christian witness to the world.

In the examples I outlined above, Evolution and Climate Change, what we see happening is that an assumed outcome is used inductively: [Evolution or Man-made Climate Change] must be true; therefore my observations and experiments must be made to fit that conclusion. Proper science can never proceed on such a premise.

NULLIUS IN VERBA, "On the word of no man", is the motto of the Royal Society, and rightly so. A scientist should never investigate just if something is *true;* he must investigate if it is either *true* or *false.*

There is nothing wrong with having a theory or a hypothesis, but then the scientist must test that theory to destruction if he can. Otherwise he picks and chooses only the observations or experimental results that fit the theory.

If we can see that this is correct then we must also look in our own back yard: if we assume that creation took place in six days a few thousand years ago and then only find evidence that suits our assumption we are behaving every bit as unscientifically as the evolutionist or 'climate-warmist'. We, like they, are putting philosophy before the science. They want to show God doesn't exist or they want to save the planet. We want to honour the God who exists and is the Creator. But if we do this at the expense of scientific integrity then, though God is God, our witness to him becomes tarnished. For he is the God of science too.

Now I realise that by saying this I am raising all kinds of hackles!

But as Jesus said,

"Why do you look at the speck of sawdust in your brother's eye and pay no attention to the plank in your own eye?"

Lk 6:41

If we insist on placing over all our scientific endeavour the theory that the earth was created in six twenty-four hour periods about 6000 years ago, we are acting no differently from the Evolutionist who is doing the same with his theory. If scientific knowledge is pursued honestly and without prejudice then God will be glorified.

In any theory put forward in science, it is the weaknesses that will be examined and tested the hardest. And that is as it should be.

"Suppose one of you wants to build a tower. Will he not first sit down and estimate the cost to see if he has enough money to complete it? For if he lays the foundation and is not able to finish it, everyone who sees it will ridicule him. ..."

Lk 14:28-29

So I must address the Young Earth Theory and must go hardest at its weakest points.

"The blessings of your father
have surpassed the blessings of my ancestors
up to the utmost bound of the everlasting hills;
may they be on the head of Joseph,
and on the crown of the head of the one
distinguished among his brothers."
Gen 49:26 NASB

Chapter 4

The Young Earth Theory

History

Until the seventeenth century most biblical scholars, indeed most Christians or most of Europe even, would doubtless have accepted the view that Genesis suggested a six-day creation some 6000 years ago (Archbishop Ussher's date based on the genealogies).

But then came the beginnings of scientific research. Partly as a result of the need for raw materials, coal and iron ore etc., the study of rocks, Geology, began to take on a proper scientific shape. The remains (fossils) of animals and fishes in the limestone rocks in the Alps and elsewhere were of course known about, but it was assumed they were formed like that and never lived, or were perhaps remnants of Noah's Flood, or just mysteries. As some of the fossils were of creatures that were unknown, some suggested that these rocks were 'God's lumber rooms' where he kept plans of creatures yet to be made or had discarded and never made; a slightly amusing but rather bizarre theory! Others, as mentioned above, first thought that they were evidence of Noah's Flood, but there were some serious difficulties with this. One being why so many fossils were fishes and molluscs (shellfish, prawn-like creatures etc.): they surely could not have drowned in the Flood? It was land creatures and birds that Noah was to take into the Ark:

18 "But I will establish my covenant with you, and you will enter the ark—you and your sons and your wife and your sons' wives with you.

19 You are to bring into the ark two of all living creatures, male and female, to keep them alive with you.

20 Two of every kind of bird, of every kind of animal and of every kind of creature that moves along the ground will come to you to be kept alive.

21 You are to take every kind of food that is to be eaten and store it away as food for you and for them."

22 Noah did everything just as God commanded him.

Gen 6:18–22

Geologists through the 18th century began to work out how the rocks they were studying were formed: they classified them into *igneous, metamorphic* and *sedimentary* types.

Igneous rocks are those that come from volcanic eruptions: essentially spewing out rock from the liquid mantle onto the surface—these do not contain fossils. Just occasionally they may contain lumps of surface sedimentary rock scooped up by molten lava which may retain their fossils.

Metamorphic rocks are cooked rocks—heated by the earth's internal heat so as to recrystallize sedimentary rocks. Thus marble is cooked limestone ($CaCO_3$), alabaster is cooked gypsum ($CaSO_4$), flint is cooked clay (Silicates) and so on. Flints can contain fossils, but usually they are distorted or destroyed by the heating process.

Sedimentary rocks are the kinds of rocks that are made from slowly built up layers of sediment, such as sand or clay carried down in rivers into lakes or oceans, or limestones made from the slow deposit of tiny calcium carbonate shells from sea creatures falling to the ocean beds. These are the rocks that contain fossils.

Geologists realised it took thousands upon thousands of years and huge depths of sediment to turn these sludges into solid rock such as sandstones, shales, limestones etc. The fossils embedded in them could not therefore have come from a single flood.

By simple calculations it was possible, by observing contemporary rates of sediment being deposited, to get an estimate as to how old some of the rock formations were: the figures were not thousands of years, but often hundreds of thousands, even millions of years. By the end of the 18th century it was reasonably clear that the earth must be many millions of years old. It was also becoming possible to date many sedimentary rocks relative to each other (ie which layer was older than which) by the types of fossils found in each layer as well as by the order the layers appeared in various rock strata. From what became known as the fossil record it was also reasonably clear that the earliest fossils were those of relatively simple creatures and later fossils more complex life forms. Though earlier simple creatures could be found in later rocks, the later life forms were never found in earlier rocks. From this came the idea called Succession—never, please, to be confused with Evolution. Succession is a deduction from careful observations; Evolution is a hypothesis attempting to explain Succession.

How were Christians reacting to these discoveries? In a variety of ways. Some merely mocked the geologists by saying that God had planted the fossils to "confound the wicked geologists": that God was deliberately deceiving them. Others began to look more carefully at Genesis and its interpretation. One noted Scottish theologian promoted the rather strange idea I touched on earlier: what is called the 'gap theory': that the fossils were the remains of the older over-written creation, but the account from Genesis Ch.1v.3ff was still a six-day process. This seemed to get over the difficulty of the age of the rocks and was perhaps adequate at the time. But geologists could find no evidence of this gap in creation—the geological record showed no unique boundary. So by the early 1840s the idea was abandoned by most Bible-believing Christians in favour of a different interpretation of the Days of Creation: what is usually called the Day-Age interpretation. This view has sound Biblical exegesis to support it and we will look in more detail at the exegesis later on in the book; but for now we need to continue to trace the historical progress of geology and Genesis.

By the 1850s this view was accepted by many Evangelical Christians. They accepted that the earth was very old and that such a position need not conflict with Genesis.

Charles Darwin: *On the Origin of Species*

In 1859 one of the most influential books on the history of life on earth was published: *On the Origin of Species*. The book contained Charles Darwin's theory of Evolution. Without a doubt this idea was radical and challenging to orthodox Christian belief in many ways. Later in the book we will look at the details of the challenge and see why, though Evolutionary theory often looks plausible, it is in reality a philosophy driving a theory, which is bad science.

But the book provoked a true storm. The theory relied, indeed required, huge amounts of time for the claimed mutations and adaptations to take place, and it seemed that the science of geology with its ancient earth had handed Darwin's theory victory on a plate.

Understandably many Bible-believing Christians felt betrayed by their acceptance of the geological time scales. Had they not made a mistake in straying away from a literalistic interpretation of Genesis? Had they not sown the wind and reaped the whirlwind?

Philip Gosse had thought so all along and, a year before *Origin* was published, had himself published a book, *Omphalos,* proposing a remarkable theory reconciling Genesis and geology.

Gosse was a Christian and became a Plymouth Brother. Though self-taught he was a very able biologist, writing *An Introduction to Zoology* for SPCK in 1847. He was a gifted communicator and a real enthusiast and was not unlike his contemporary, Hugh Miller, a Christian geologist and writer, though of a very different view regarding the age of the earth. Gosse was made a member of the Royal Society.

His book *Omphalos* (a Greek word meaning navel) remains a curious aberration in many ways, though a valiant effort to try and cut the knot of the Genesis interpretation of a Young Earth and geology.

His thesis was very bold. He proposed the idea that when God created Adam he created him with a navel, even though Adam was a direct creation and had never been born in the natural way. From this hypothesis, that God created Adam with the appearance of a natural origin of gestation and birth even though his creation was in reality instantaneous, he extrapolated the idea that God had created the rocks and the solar system with the same mature quality or apparent age. Sedimentary rocks, for example, might look as if they had taken millions of years to build up in layers, but in fact they had appeared instantaneously in that condition. Thus geologists were only observing and calculating an *appearance* of age, not a reality.

It was an ingenious theory and certainly cut the knot of interpretation of Genesis Ch.1.

But it never really found much acceptance amongst Bible-believing Christians, despite the publication of *On the Origin of Species* the next year.

The difficulties with his theory were considerable. By cutting one knot it unfortunately tied up several more.

1. His thesis was based not on Scripture itself but on a *conjecture* concerning Adam's navel about which Scripture was silent.
2. It made scientific investigations of the past, particularly geology, more or less redundant. Whatever they might look like, he said that nearly all rocks were a mere 6000 years old.
3. Viewed more critically, it did seem to hint that God was a bit of a deceiver: putting in virtual age. Why was that needed? What purpose did this virtual age serve? One thinks of slightly shady antiques dealers 'ageing' paintings or furniture to give them a provenance they did not warrant. It echoed the more abusive Christian response to the science of geology which claimed God had placed fossils in the rocks to deceive geologists!
4. It presented huge difficulties for astronomers. By the 1800s the universe was 'getting bigger'. The speed of light had been determined. Distances to nearby stars were beginning to be measured and the distances were mind-boggling. So much so that stellar distances began to be measured in light years: the distance travelled by a beam of light in one year (nearly 6,000,000,000,000 miles). In 1813 the Astronomer Royal William Herschel commented to the poet Thomas Campbell, "I have observed stars of which the light, it can be proved, must take two million years to reach the earth." Our own spiral galaxy, the Milky Way, is about 200,000 light years across.

Today we are able to observe distant galaxies that are billions of light years away. In 1996 the Hubble Deep Field telescope, for six days, 'bored' into a tiny area of the sky, likened to 'a grain of sand held at arm's length', where no terrestrial telescopes had detected any object. The results were staggering. In the tiny 'hole' the HDF detected nearly two thousand new galaxies. Up till then the estimate had been that the Universe might contain a mere ten billion galaxies. After the six days' exposure of the HDF this estimate jumped to fifty billion! Not only did the HDF detect their distance, but also this 'bore hole' was a bore hole in time: the light from some of these galaxies set out nearly thirteen *billion* years ago.*

> * The small red objects in the picture on the back cover (*Hubble* UDF) are galaxies so far away that their blue light has become red. They are travelling away from us at speeds approaching 150,000 km s^{-1} (half the speed of light).

Astronomers, by the 1860s, were starting to use spectroscopy to find out what stars were made of using the information from the light that was coming from them.

This puts enormous pressure on the mature creation thesis: creating Adam as a mature adult was one thing, but to create stars whose light takes millions of years, even billions of years, to reach the earth raises a pretty daunting question mark over the idea.

To suggest, as some have in recent times, that God created the stars with 'light already on the way' pushes hard at the boundaries of reason. Light is information from and about its source. It's as if, when a new Postal Delivery Company is set up, suddenly the towns and streets contain postmen with letters in their bags from people who have at exactly the same time popped into existence. It does seem highly improbable that God would act in this way.

Omphalos was not a success, unlike the books of his fellow Christian and geologist Hugh Miller about Genesis and creation, which continued to sell for fifty years after the author's death in 1856. Copies are still sought after today.

After the upset of Darwin's *Origin*, Bible-believing Christians, for the most part, returned to the idea of ancient Creation. Some, it is true, decided to accommodate Darwin's theory, a position usually called Theistic Evolution. It had one or two surprising advocates: the great theological scholar on the verbal inspiration of Scripture, B. B. Warfield, embraced Theistic Evolution.

Then in the 1960s books began appearing relaunching the Young Earth Theory. Names such as Whitcombe, Morris and Monty White appeared on the radar. Books such as *The Genesis Flood* put forward the Young Earth Theory with considerable gusto. Although they seldom laid any claim to be following the Gosse theory, his ghost was certainly hovering in the wings.

These books presented to the layman what looked like knock-down arguments against Evolution primarily based on disproving an ancient earth. Graphs and tables, equations and data appeared alleging that the earth is no more than 6000-10,000 years old.

Essential to Darwin's theory was the need for time, lots of it. Remove that option, recent creationists suggested, and Evolutionary theory is dead in the water.

In any conflict of ideas it is important to know the weak points of the opposition and address those. My question is whether the idea of the earth being very old is weakly attested and therefore the right point to attack. Unfortunately it is not. The scientific evidence for an ancient earth is absolutely overwhelming. If we might employ a military metaphor: it is a truly well fortified position. In 1939 the French Maginot Line was so strong that it would have been military folly to make a frontal assault, so the Germans attacked the flank—which was undefended (by going through Holland and Belgium). The Young Earth theory makes a tactical error by its frontal assault on an impregnable position, when in fact the flank of Evolutionary theory is very exposed if only people knew it.

Central to the Young Earth Theory is the Fall and the Flood. The theory is principally addressing physical, geological and biological processes and not the spiritual and moral aspects: it is trying to proceed in a scientific manner in describing what happened at the physical level. That is not a problem as science is not designed to be theology. But the aim is to be consistent with what the Bible says.

The theory proposes that at the Fall there followed a cataclysmic upheaval on the earth and a sudden shift in the way the Laws of Nature behaved. It is claimed, for example, that up till the Fall, the laws of thermodynamics were not operating as they do now, and that the Fall introduced Entropy into the Universe as part of the judgement on Adam. This idea will be explored later.

Secondly, the Flood event is considered responsible for creating all the fossils, many of the mountains (some occurred after the Fall) and all the coal and oil resources we now enjoy. During the Flood huge mountain ranges were formed; volcanoes below the sea spewed out molten lava, boiling the waters and thereby presumably killing all the fish.

On this idea, when Noah and his family emerged from the Ark, the geography of the earth would have been quite unrecognisable: the whole planet had been totally rearranged.

Before we go on to look in some detail at parts of this theory, we need to address the question whether the theory is consistent with what the Bible says.

There are some quite difficult issues.

1. There is no mention in Genesis of a planet-wide physical cataclysm following the Fall of man. Adam and Eve are expelled from the Garden under sentence of death. The Garden was clearly a special place, unlike the rest of the earth.

2. On the plus side, Paul maybe does hint at a kind of disruption in Rom 8:19–22:

   19 The creation waits in eager expectation for the sons of God to be revealed.
   20 For the creation was subjected to frustration, not by its own choice, but by the will of the one who subjected it, in hope
   21 that the creation itself will be liberated from its bondage to decay and brought into the glorious freedom of the children of God.
   22 We know that the whole creation has been groaning as in the pains of childbirth right up to the present time.

   But whether Paul is saying this bondage started at the Fall is not quite so clear, nor whether he had in mind thermodynamic processes.

3. When Noah was instructed to build the Ark, God tells him, *"So make yourself an ark of cypress wood; make rooms in it and*

coat it with pitch inside and out." Gen 6:14. If, as the catastrophists claim, oil and coal were formed during the Flood, this would have presented Noah with a big problem of supply. Where to get the pitch which is a form of oil? In view of the size of the Ark (450ft or more long) he would have needed quite a lot of it.

4. Geography: if the Flood really did do all that the catastrophists claim—rearranging the whole planet—how come two great rivers of the Middle East, the Tigris and the Euphrates, remained in place after the Flood? Just luck? A special miracle?

5. Miracle: the Young Earth Theory claims to explain geology and biology after Creation itself without resorting to miracle, but rather to natural processes we can study today. Therefore it would not be appropriate for the theory to get round the problems outlined above by resorting to 'special miracles'. Science, by definition, cannot study miracles, not because they do not happen, but because they are special activities of God introduced into the natural realm and are by definition beyond what science can investigate as they are not repeatable.

6. In its favour is that it interprets the Flood as global—this being, at least superficially, what the Bible implies.

All in all, the Young Earth's use of the Fall as a physical catastrophe along with the Flood only partly fits with Scripture but requires extra-scriptural insertions, at least one of which—oil being created during the Flood—raises a difficulty with the scriptural account. This does not disqualify it. Conjectures in interpreting scientific data are sometimes allowable.

Theologically the Young Earth Theory deals neatly with what might be described as the Problem of Death before the Fall: there was no death before the Fall. But what seems a neat solution still leaves some questions: was Adam created mortal or immortal?

It deals too with the issue of the meaning of the Hebrew word *yom*, Day: it is a twenty-four hour period. Again this seems to neatly dispose of the issue, but the text of Genesis Chs.1-3 leaves us with some nagging questions nonetheless: why is the same word, *yom*, used in at least three different ways?

To mean Day as opposed to Night (12 hours),

To mean Day as a twenty-four hour period.

To mean six days: *This is the account of the heavens and the earth when they were created, in the day (yom) that the LORD God made earth and heaven.* Gen 2:4 NASB.

And to mean a rather more extended period. Adam is told, *"in the day [yom] you eat of it you will surely die."* Yet he lives some 900 years after that. Further, what meaning could Adam attach to "you will surely die" if he had never seen anything die or anything dead? The word 'die', for him, would have no context, no meaning. Surely God would not give Adam a command with a sanction that was incomprehensible?

Let us now step back a bit and look more widely at the Young Earth Theory. In broad outline it proposes the following:

1. In the six days (24-hour periods) between 6-10,000 years ago God created the heavens and the earth. During that first week everything created was a direct act of God—we will use the term miracle here as shorthand.

2. From that point on laws of nature came into play: rocks eroded, winds blew, plants and animals grew and reproduced. These phenomena can be studied by science as they were proceeding according to laws, not miracle.

3. When Adam fell, further laws of nature came into existence—perhaps in particular the 2nd and 3rd laws of thermodynamics. As Scripture does not tell us how long after Day Six Adam fell, it is not clear whether the laws of nature in 2. and the additional laws such as those of thermodynamics in 3. were separated by any appreciable period of time.

4. When God brought the Flood, its physical effects were caused entirely according to the laws of nature and its effects can be studied today using those laws.

Creation Science therefore must focus its research and study from 2. onwards, ie when the laws of nature as we observe them today came into operation, taking over from the Creation regime of the Six days which was essentially miracle.

The fundamental question for Creation Science is to distinguish between physical phenomena, such as rock formations, stars, galaxies etc. which were created in the six days (and are therefore miraculous) and those phenomena which are the results of 2. and 3. This is not an easy distinction to work out.

If we use a telescope and look into the heavens we are not only looking into distance but also looking back in time. Light travels at 300,000 km/s and is the Universe's top speed. Light from the sun reaches us some eight minutes after it leaves the sun's surface. Light from the sun takes more than four hours to reach Neptune, the most distant planet in the solar system (now that Pluto has been demoted). The nearest star, Proxima Centauri, is some four light years away (the light from the star taking four years to reach us) and distant objects observed by the Hubble telescope are several billion light years away. Or at least so it would appear, unless we are mistaking what obeys the laws of nature and what is miracle—which, on the Young Earth Theory, we must be doing. But again there is no visible shift observable with our telescopes as we pass beyond the 6000 light year divider. Incidentally, a sphere, radius 6000 light years, centred on our solar system is only a tiny portion of the spiral galaxy (the Milky Way) our solar system is part of and through which it moves. If normal laws apply it is 200,000 light years across and about 12,000 light years thick (it is like a starfish—wider than it is tall) containing between 200-400 billion stars. Beyond our galaxy there are billions of other galaxies stretching out in all directions to unimaginable distances.

Attempts are made to get round this enormous difficulty. In 2007 Dr. John Hartnett published an intriguing book, *Starlight, Time and the New Physics*. The idea behind his book goes back to an article, 'Binary Stars and the velocity of light', by Parry Moon of the Massachusetts Institute of Technology and Domina E. Spencer of the University of Connecticut published in the *Journal of the Optical Society of America*, August, 1953, vol. V-43, pp. 635-41.

In most of their paper Moon and Spencer discuss the evidence for and against Einstein's special theory of relativity, of which they disapproved at the time (this was 1953, and the evidence for special relativity then was not so overwhelming as it is today). Having reached the conclusion that Einstein could not be faulted, they turned, in their last couple of pages, to their revolutionary suggestion. In effect, they asked the question: 'Is it possible to conceive of any kind of a universe where Einstein's theory would appear to be true, when it was actually false?' Yes, it is, they concluded. *If* there were two quite different kinds of space co-existing, superimposed on each other, (1) ordinary space and (2) curved Riemannian space (the latter is a construction in pure mathematics); and *if* the stars were positioned in the ordinary space while light travelled through the Riemannian space; and *if* the Riemannian space (which in theory could have any curvature that you might like to assign to it) just happened to have a radius of curvature of five light years—if space were like that, then nobody could prove Einstein wrong. Another odd consequence of such a universe, they pointed out, would be that light could travel right across it by travelling only 5π (15.71) light years.*

Notice the three *if*'s. Building hypothesis on hypothesis is always dubious in science and a triple series like this is definitely in the realm of wildest speculation.

Moon and Spencer seem to have regarded it as a mere mathematical curiosity. Having slipped it into that paper they let the matter drop and never returned to it again. And the world of science showed no interest in it, except Young Earth theorists who have run with it. Faced with this misuse of the Moon and Spencer paper, papers by several writers have appeared, setting the record straight. In particular, D. J. Krause points out that experimental work by Brecher in X-ray astronomy in 1977 showed that Moon and Spencer's suggestion is invalidated. The astrophysicist Dr Perry Phillips also cited a number of reports of experimental work which, he said, proved conclusively that the Moon and Spencer speculation cannot be right.*

* See Alan Hayward, *Creation and Evolution*, p. 106-107.

What needs to be understood is that it is not science fact but speculation by Moon and Spencer—an amusing aside for them and nothing else. Even the term 'Reimannian space' is misleading in that it is merely referring to theoretical mathematical topological geometry not to the physical space of our universe.

Of course, using this mathematical construct one can produce lots of self-consistent mathematics that is quite impressive, but it proves nothing about reality. It is very doubtful anyway that the maths in Hartnett's book is understood by many of his readers.

To use it to *prove* a young earth is to make the elementary mistake of Descartes who proceeded by first using his imagination as to how things *might* be (like the Greek philosophers did), then to use mathematics to see if the imagined reality was mathematically consistent: if it was then, according to him, the imagined reality must be true. Darwin did the same and Global Warmists are doing the same today (for them, substitute computer programs for imagination).

But there is an even more devastating piece of evidence, astronomically much closer to home, facing Young Earth theorists.

As mentioned earlier, it takes light about eight minutes to travel from the sun to the earth. The source of this light comes from the centre of the sun, which is an enormous fusion reactor running at a temperature of 15 million degrees. Here 10% of the sun's mass is condensed in a plasma* ten times as dense as the centre of the earth.

* **Plasma** - see glossary page 227.

JET (the Joint European Torus, located in Culham near Oxford) generates plasma from hydrogen and subjects it to extreme temperatures (in excess of 40 million degrees) to produce nuclear fusion. Containing the plasma is, as can be imagined, extremely challenging. It is done by forcing the plasma into a magnetic 'bottle' using very powerful magnetic fields. This prevents the plasma from coming into contact with any physical surface.

This is not guesswork or theory; these are facts deduced from direct measurements. Scientists make use of the sun's 'hum': the hum is made up of what one might call seismic sound vibrations involving the whole body of the sun. From these vibrations along with other means of measurement the nature of the sun's interior has been fully mapped.

The light that reaches us from the sun cannot be travelling through Riemannian space—even if such a thing were to exist: the measurement of speed and distance rules that out completely. So the sun and the earth are interacting in normal space.*

* Similar hums have now been detected in other stars.
One is put in mind of the words from Job 38:7 (NASB)
...*When the morning stars sang together,*
And all the sons of God shouted for joy...

Now here is the really interesting part. The photons (light particles) that set off from the sun's surface to reach the earth have taken *at least 200,000 years* to come up from the central fusion reactor to the surface. This is a fact, not a theory. The sun's central fusion reactor could switch off tomorrow and humanity would notice no difference for at least 200,000 years (the Lord tarrying of course). Only scientists observing highly elusive particles called neutrinos would notice their disappearance, indicating that fusion had stopped. It follows, as clearly as night follows day, that the sun must have pre-existed us by a minimum of 200,000 years for us to be receiving any light at all!

The stars themselves come in an enormous variety of sizes, the very big ones lasting the shortest length of time (perhaps a mere hundred million years) before exploding as supernovas and collapsing into neutron stars or even black holes. As they do so they shower the galaxy with the products of their huge nuclear furnaces. These fuse hydrogen into heavier elements such as carbon and iron (the heaviest element to be produced by fusion in a star's interior). When they explode the shock waves in turn smash these elements together and produce another fifty or so even heavier elements, some of them radioactive, such as uranium. Without these processes there would have been no basic materials to form planets and from which God could create life. We are literally made from dust, as the Bible says.

Our own sun is just right: not too big, not too small and has already lasted five billion years or so and could go on for several billion more. It is also fairly well out on one of the spiral arms of our Galaxy,

34   CHAPTER 4

not too near the centre, which is far more crowded with stars and gas and dust, itself forming new stars even as you read these words. It is just as well that we are this far out as the radiation levels in the centre of the Galaxy would wipe out all life on earth.

All the preceding description must however be wrong according to the Young Earth Theory. Only the last 6000 years follow the laws of nature; the rest just appeared in six days, fully formed with the light 'on the way'.

Perhaps those who are already chafing at my descriptions will at least allow me this: that the heavens are older than the earth itself. "In the beginning God created the *heavens* and the earth." Could we allow that the Universe itself is very ancient, perhaps 13.7 billion years old? The earth could still be recent. But is it? Let us return to earth.

The Age of the Earth

The Haymond sedimentary rock formation in the USA is less than a mile thick but extends over a large area and contains more than 30,000 alternating layers of shale and sandstone, two entirely different types of sedimentary rock. Shale is made of compacted clay.

However the formation came about, the alternations suggest strongly seasonal variations of sand and clay silt (between 1mm and 5mm thicknesses) slowly settling in deep water. So using conventional geology one could assume the formation took possibly 15,000 years to form. The question is how much was formed naturally *after* the six days and how much was miracle. One must assume the first 18,000 layers were by miracle, but there is no obvious discontinuity at the change-over point in the actual strata.

Despite a variety of attempts to do so, Flood geology is not able to account for this rock formation. One or two Creation Science websites [eg www.creationontheweb.com] refer to an article in *Science* magazine [318(5857):1734-1735 2007] about mud deposition during flooding which suggests that mud can be 'painted' across a lake bed in fast flowing turbulent conditions and leave behind a fairly stable layer. But no flood can rapidly deposit thin layers first of fine clay and then of fine sand on top of each other with no appreciable mixing between the layers, switching over *every five minutes* as would be required by the Flood hypothesis to create the Haymond formation. So we are left wanting to know which part is miracle and which part is natural. There is no scientific way of knowing and the Bible doesn't seem that concerned to tell us either!

The Bible is not against the study of the natural world. King Solomon was, amongst many other things, a scientist of a kind:

"He described plant life, from the cedar of Lebanon to the hyssop that grows out of walls. He also taught about animals and birds, reptiles and fish." 1 Kings 4:33.

But this seems almost an aside, not central to the lessons God wants us to learn from the life of King Solomon.

The problem with the Young Earth Theory is that it places geologists and other scientists who study the past in a dilemma: is it even worth studying the past if we cannot tell which is natural and which is miracle? It makes the Universe lack rationality and instead seems to make it arbitrary: this river bed looks about 5000 years old—and it is, but this older river bed dated on the same principles as the first one to be about 8000 years ago can't be, so it's a miracle instead. It simply doesn't read right!

Even though he is not mentioned, Gosse's idea of mature creation is still there. The Young Earth Theory is essentially saying the same: God created certain things to look far older than they really are. And he would seem to have done it very well, in one way, because the way real geological or astronomical events, that took place according to natural laws, blend seamlessly into the 'mature creation' events created by miracle is quite astonishing.

In some ways the Young Earth Theory should leave it at that. God is almighty and if he chooses to bring about Creation in this way that is his prerogative and we should not argue with him on the matter. We must simply say that scientists should pursue sciences that do not try to go back into the past because they will not be able to obtain real scientific knowledge from it. There are, after all, plenty of areas of science, which can be very rewarding and fruitful, that need not trespass into the past.

But then those espousing the Young Earth Theory go and spoil it all! They try and *prove* that the earth is in fact young. On their understanding of Creation this should be impossible. If they do find evidence of a young earth then it rather looks like they have caught God out—he missed a bit which should have been created mature. If God really did create a mature Universe in six days some six thousand years ago, then there should surely be no physical evidence at all that this is what he did. But Creation Science books are filled up with proofs of a young earth! By so doing they unintentionally seem to show that God is not a God who is perfect in all his works, but instead is rather careless and slipshod!

Happily it is possible to remove this unintended slur on God's character! We will show with several examples, which must serve for all, that the proofs produced to support a young earth are incorrect. Not one piece shows true evidence of a young earth. Paradoxically therefore, the earth could indeed have been created according to the Young Earth theory. The 'proof' lies in the fact that there must not be any evidence for it.

Let me illustrate what I mean.

Uniformitarian Estimates of the age of the Earth

The table below (or bits of it) seems to appear in most creation science books. The idea is that the data show that the age of the earth calculated by geological methods is totally inconsistent—therefore it is wrong. Therefore the earth is young.

Table 5:1 Uniformitarian Estimates of the Age of the Earth
[from *What about origins* by Dr A.J. Monty White]
(Unless otherwise noted, based on standard assumptions of closed systems, constant rates, and no initial daughter components.)

Process	Indicated Age of Earth
1. Efflux of Helium-4 into the atmosphere	1750-175,000 years
2. influx of meteoritic dust from space	too small to calculate
3. Influx of radiocarbon to the earth system	5000-10,000 years
4. Development of total human population	less than 4000 years
5. Influx of uranium to the ocean via rivers	10,000-100,000 years
6. Influx of sodium to the ocean via rivers	260,000,000 years
7. Influx of nickel to the ocean via rivers	9000 years

8. Influx of magnesium to the ocean via rivers	45,000,000 years
9. Influx of silicon to the ocean via rivers	8000 years
10. Influx of potassium to the ocean via rivers	11,000,000 years
11. Influx of copper to the ocean via rivers	50,000 years
12. Influx of gold to the ocean via rivers	560,000 years
13. Influx of silver to the ocean via rivers	2,100,000 years
14. Influx of mercury to the ocean via rivers	42,000 years
15. Influx of lead to the ocean via rivers	2000 years
16. Influx of tin to the ocean via rivers	100,000 years
17 Influx of aluminium to the ocean via rivers	100 years
18. Influx of carbonate to the ocean via rivers	100,000 years
19. Influx of sulphate to the ocean via rivers	10,000,000 years
20. Influx of chlorine to the ocean via rivers	164,000,000 years
21. Influx of calcium to the ocean via rivers	1,000,000 years
22. Leaching of sodium from continents	32,000,000 years
23. Leaching of chlorine from continents	1,000,000 years
24. Leaching of calcium from continents	12,000,000 years
25. Influx of sediment to the ocean via rivers	30,000,000 years
26. Erosion of sediment from continents	14,000,000 years
27. Decay of earth's magnetic field	10,000 years
28. Efflux of oil from traps by fluid pressure	10,000-100,000 years
29. Formation of radiogenic lead by neutron capture	too small to measure
30. Formation of radiogenic Sr by neutron capture	too small to measure
31. Decay of natural remanent paleomagnetism	100,000 years
32. Decay of C-14 in pre-cambrian wood	4000 years
33. Decay of uranium with initial lead	too small to measure
34. Decay of potassium with entrapped argon	too small to measure
35. Influx of juvenile water to oceans	340,000,000 years
36. Influx of magma from mantle to form crust	500,000,000 years
37. Growth of active coral reefs	10,000 years
38. Growth of oldest living part of biosphere	5000 years
39. Origin of human civilizations	5000 years
40. Formation of river deltas	5000 years
41. Submarine oil seepage into oceans	50,000,000 years
42. Decay of natural plutonium	80,000,000 years
43. Decay of lines of galaxies	10,000,000 years
44. Expanding interstellar gas	60,000,000 years
45. Formation of C-14 on meteorites	100,000 years
46. Decay of short-period comets	10,000 years
47. Decay of long-period comets	1,000,000 years
48. Influx of small particles to the sun	83,000 years
49. Maximum life of meteor showers	5,000,000 years
50. Accumulation of dust on the moon	200,000 years
51. Deceleration of earth by tidal friction	500,000,000 years
52. Cooling of earth by heat efflux	24,000,000 years
53. Accumulation of calcareous ooze on sea floor	5,000,000 years
54. Influx of lithium into ocean via rivers	20,000,000 years
55. Influx of titanium into ocean via rivers	160 years
56. Influx of chromium into ocean via rivers	350 years

57. Influx of manganese into ocean via rivers	1,400 years
58. Influx of iron into ocean via rivers	140 years
59. Influx of cobalt into ocean via rivers	18,000 years
60. Influx of zinc into ocean via rivers	180,000 years
61. Influx of rubidium into ocean via rivers	270,000 years
62. Influx of strontium into ocean via rivers	19,000,000 years
63. Influx of bismuth into ocean via rivers	45,000 years
64. Influx of thorium into ocean via rivers	350 years
65. Influx of antimony into ocean via rivers	350,000 years
66. Influx of tungsten into ocean via rivers	1000 years
67. Influx of barium into ocean via rivers	84,000 years
68. Influx of molybdenum into ocean via rivers	500,000 years
69. Influx of bicarbonate into ocean via rivers	700,000 years
70. Escape of high-velocity stars from globular clusters	40,000 years
71. Rotation of spiral galaxies	200,000,000 years
72. Accumulation of peat in peat bogs	8000 years
73. Accumulation of sediments for sedimentary rocks	20,000 years
74. Lithification of sediments to form sedimentary rocks	20,000 years

The trouble is that the contents of this table have nothing to do with the age of the earth. It has actually been cobbled together from several sources (some of them Creation Research sources) and given a new heading.

Most of the oceanographic data, for example, is about something quite different—it is about *residence time*. Sodium salts for example flow into the oceans and eventually exit as the oceans dry up and become part of the land.

A homely example—water flows into your house into the roof tank—it stays there until someone runs the tap and then water begins to leave the tank. If the tank holds, let us say, 150 gallons and a bath holds 15 gallons, then the time the water stays in the tank will be decided by how many baths are taken. If one bath a day, then it stays in the tank ten days, which is its *residence time*. But no-one would deduce your house is only ten days old from this!

The table headings cloud over this obvious fact and then the author states that geologists are claiming this measures the age of the earth.

The speed of light

It has been claimed by some Creation Research scientists that this has slowed down over the centuries. They mistake degrees of accuracy for change: a failure to understand a very basic concept in science.

Suppose I have a cake and I ask someone its weight. They might pick it up and estimate between one and two kilogram, perhaps about 1.5 kilogram. Then it might be weighed on a bathroom scales and register 1.8 kg. Then it is weighed on a postal scales and gives a reading of 1.827 kg and finally placed on an accurate chemical balance you get a reading of 1.82734 kg.

Clearly it would be nonsense to suggest that the cake was steadily increasing in weight! It is simply that the instruments used to weigh it are of increasing accuracy.

This is what happened with the measurement of the speed of light.

The first person to make a stab at measuring it was a Danish astronomer, Ole Römer. In 1676 he made a most elegant set of observations. Using eclipses of the moons of Jupiter (by then visible through the new telescopes), he observed their times when Jupiter was in conjunction with earth (ie on the same side of the solar system as earth) and when in opposition (on the far side). If light travelled instantaneously (as was thought at the time) then there should be no difference in the time these eclipses were observed. In fact he observed several minutes' delay, giving him the time it took the light to travel across the diameter of the earth's orbit. From this he calculated that the speed of light was 224,000 kilometre per second. Considering the relative crudity of the telescopes and clocks, the vagaries of weather allowing observations, and the still rather approximate calculations of orbit diameters, this was a remarkable result. The modern measurement of the speed of light is about 300,000 kilometre per second. Many experiments to measure the speed of light have taken place since Römer's experiment, each honing the level of accuracy. The current value is 299,790 km/sec to six significant figures. The claim is made in most Creation Science books that the speed of light has *slowed down* since creation, when it was infinite. As the figures above clearly show, if they want to use the argument that the speed has changed then it has *speeded up*, not slowed down!

Reversal of the Earth's Magnetic Field

This is another 'favourite'. The earth's magnetic field is at present diminishing in strength (figures for the last 150 years are available). Creation Research Society scientist Thomas Barnes claimed that by extrapolating back from these figures he could demonstrate that the value of the field 20,000 years ago would have been impossibly high. Unfortunately he used an exponential curve in a way which no serious scientist could justify from the data. With data points for just the last 100 years on a graph (and these are fairly scattered at that), he then 'fits' his curve and then draws it backwards in time to his 20,000 year point. The real data on his graph is less than 0.05% of the line. Further, if he had used a straight line (just as easy to fit) the graph he would have got would have been nearer 100,000,000 years, which did not fit his preconceived theory of a young earth. Even more unfortunately, it is known that the earth's Magnetic Field has reversed itself many times in the past—and may be due to reverse again fairly soon.

The evidence for this is contained in solidified magmas which come out of tectonic trenches in the oceans. These contain fragments of magnetic mineral which, though once liquid under the crust, solidified on breaking surface—'freezing' evidence of the magnetic orientation and strength at that time. These clearly show fluctuations (there are times when the field tries to reverse and fails; called a Laschamp Excursion—see pages 206-207) and reversals of the field.

Second Law of thermodynamics

The Second Law of thermodynamics is much misused. The Law states that *in a closed system* entropy always tends to increase.

Entropy is not an easy property to understand. It is a measurement of the disorder in a system (*system* is a word used to cover anything from a chemical reaction to a heat engine or to the planet or even the Universe: any situation where any kind of energy is being exchanged).

It is measured in Joule K⁻¹, energy/degree temperature (K is what is called Absolute Temperature where 0 is Absolute zero temperature, no heat energy at all in the system. On the Centigrade scale, which assigns 0°C to the freezing point of water, Absolute zero is -273°C).

An example of entropy in action is the melting of ice. When ice melts the molecules of water which form a crystalline solid start to break apart to form liquid: a much more chaotic slurry of water molecules. The disorder in the system increases and the ordered solid becomes a disordered liquid. In order to melt, however, heat energy is needed to enable the process: but the temperature of the ice/water mixture as it melts remains constant at 0°C (or 273K). Energy is going into the system of ice and water, but the temperature does not change. All the energy is going in to the creation of disorder: the entropy change.*

* The energy required to convert 1kg of ice into 1kg of water at 273K is called the Latent Heat and the entropy change (ΔS) is given by:

Latent Heat of ice 333,000 Joule per kilogram of ice

$$\Delta S = \frac{333,000}{273} = 1220 \text{ J K}^{-1} \text{ kg}^{-1} \text{ of ice}$$

If you have a hot and a cold body together heat flows from the hotter to the cooler and in the end both will reach the same temperature and therefore no 'work' can be got out of the system at maximum entropy. The energy available in a system that can do work is given the name Free Energy (G). Chemical Free Energy is required to sustain life; therefore life cannot be sustained in a closed system (shut a mouse in an airtight box without food or water and it will quickly die). This is then applied to the earth by saying therefore life could not be produced naturally or sustained as entropy would tend to destroy it. This is bad science.

The earth is not a closed system—it receives huge amounts of energy from the sun—far more than is needed to sustain the complexity of life.

Every day the earth operates a huge heat engine moving billions of tons of water from the oceans into the atmosphere and then condensing it as rain or snow.

Result: salt water is distilled into pure water: a local reversal of entropy—impossible in a closed system, but quite possible in an open system.

Moon dust

The idea that there should have been hundreds of feet of dust on the moon is unfortunately based on another fallacy.

A Young Earth scientist called Slusher (writing in 1980) claimed that, according to a Swedish geophysicist called Hans Petterson, it was estimated that 14,300,000 ton of cosmic dust fell on the earth each year. A similar but undisturbed layer of dust should presumably coat the surface of the moon. On this basis, if the earth was four billion years old there should be a layer of dust nearly 100 feet thick on the moon. The science fiction writer Arthur C. Clarke even wrote a novel (in the 1960s), *A Fall of Moondust*, based on this possibility. But as the dust found on the moon was nothing like such a depth (it was only a few inches) it showed that the moon, and therefore the earth, was young.

First note that Petterson was giving an estimate—a semi-informed *guess*. Second, that the estimate had been made before 1961. By 1980 real figures for the cosmic dust had long since been obtained from measurements made by satellites as part of the preparations for the Apollo missions. The real data showed how wildly wrong Petterson's estimate had been! The actual figure for dust falling on the earth was a mere 16,000 ton per year—sufficient only to coat the earth with a layer of dust a few inches thick—the moon similarly—assuming the earth to be about four billion years old. So the moon dust theory 'crumbles to dust' and in fact the amount of dust on the moon definitely provides straightforward evidence for a very old moon! It also needs to be stated that Slusher ought to have known these facts.

Further, here is an instance of Young Earth scientists being inconsistent. They often criticise geologists for depending on Uniformitarianism: the idea that geological processes that have taken place in the past took place at the same rate as can be observed going on now. Rates of erosion etc. Young Earth scientists claim that this is wrong (because it makes the earth too old). However, "sauce for the goose is sauce for the gander", they are only too happy to use the principle if they think it will suit them!

The Flood - again

As touched on earlier the Young Earth Theory harnesses the Flood to provide explanations for a huge number of geological structures. It is argued that, during the Flood, the whole earth was rearranged geologically—in a vastly speeded up version of plate tectonics theory. Mountains were formed at an incredible speed after the rapid deposition of huge thickness of fossil-bearing rock—hence the marine fossils found high up in the Andes, Himalayas and Alps, for example. Coincident with the Flood was an incredible explosion of vulcanism, responsible for cooking all the marine fossils before they were buried under sedimentary detritus from the Flood. After the waters subsided the whole planet had been completely rearranged; vast layers of extremely rapidly formed sedimentary and metamorphic rock had been upturned and twisted, vast deposits of coal and oil had been formed, and buried in thousands of feet of rock and silt: for Noah and his family it must have been like emerging from a spaceship onto a completely different planet. The result of the vulcanism was to shroud the earth in dust and water vapour which, by shutting out the sunlight, ushered in an Ice Age—the only one, according to the Young Earth Theory.

Such a scenario is possible in principle—our God is infinitely powerful. But is there evidence from either the Scriptures or science for this scenario?

The Scriptures

1. There is no mention of the vulcanism.
2. There is no mention of the sun not shining after the Flood—quite the reverse: in Gen 9:12, the rainbow cannot appear without the sun. The normal cycle of the seasons is affirmed by God in Gen 8:22.
3. There is no mention of the need for Noah to receive on board any sea or freshwater creatures. Remember the animals *came to* the Ark (Gen 7:9). God makes it clear that the Flood would

destroy only air-breathing creatures: Gen 6:17—note it says 'everything on land'—not therefore in the seas.

4. Despite the theory's complete rearrangement of the globe, the rivers Tigris and Euphrates (Gen 2:14) remain as recognisable geographical features after the Flood.

5. The Flood is supposed to have created all the coal and oil deposits on the planet. From where, then, did Noah get his pitch before the Flood? (Gen 6:14).

6. Vegetation clearly re-established itself very quickly. Indeed, an olive tree survived the inundation (Gen 8:11) to emerge, still living, from the receding waters. However, the catastrophic picture of the Flood would render the planet infertile for years or even millennia as all the topsoil would either be buried under huge rock deposits or so scattered as to be effectively non-existent.

The Science

There are many objections raised by scientific data to this idea, but I will content myself with just one.

There is an estimated 500 million gigaton of limestone (calcium carbonate) in and on the earth's crust. That is about 80 ton m^{-2} over the whole surface of the planet. Limestone is formed from the remains of marine seashells and skeletons. The Young Earth Theory says these creatures died in the Flood and were formed into limestone.

If we make a very modest and conservative assumption that the living sea creatures from which the limestone was formed were the same volume as their crushed shells or skeletons (in reality it is likely to be ten to a hundred times the volume) then we come up with an incredible figure. For all these creatures to be formed into limestone during one year, they must have all been living simultaneously. These living creatures would have had no space to live in! They would form a concentrated mass of living animals 80m (250ft) high over the entire surface of the globe—land and sea. And this is but the beginning of the problems. The sum of all the other fossils that we know of would face similar difficulties if all the animals were to be alive at the same time.

And remember, fossils themselves are a tiny proportion of all the creatures that have lived and died. The Flood geology hypothesis simply doesn't work.

When an idea or a theory stubs its toe against reality, it is time to re-examine the premise of the theory.

1. It is trying to reconcile science with an *interpretation* of Genesis.
2. It is trying to defeat Darwinism (Evolutionary theory) by removing the long time spans that standard geology would make available.

If we can reassess this second point, maybe we can also reassess the interpretation used for Genesis.

In the late 18th and early 19th centuries, geologists were very practical people. Their reason for studying rocks was often because they were prospecting for minerals, iron ore, coal, tin, gold, diamonds etc. But some also went out into the field from sheer love of the subject. Both were usually excellent observers and experimenters.

The conclusions of these men were that if currently observed processes of erosion, sedimentation etc. were anything to go by, then the earth's rocks were very old indeed: names such as Hutton, Cuvier, Agassiz, later Lyell and many others had begun to put geology onto a solid scientific basis. They had charted out the types and ages of rocks and had begun to construct what is known as the geological column. This is a theoretical chart of all the known rock types and their dates in relation to one another. Nowhere on the earth does such a column exist complete. Rather, the complete column was pieced together from fragmentary bits of such a column. To illustrate using a simple analogy:

Suppose there are 26 rock types which we will label *A, B, C ... X, Y, Z,* with *A* being the earliest and *Z* the most recent.

The column consists of all 26 letters, but the earth only has fragments. So in one place a geologist finds *CDEFG,* in another he finds *ABCD,* in another he finds *FGHIJ,* in another *GHIJKLMNO,* etc. The fragments nearly always show the same order of rock types.

Within many of these rocks there are fossil remains. As mentioned earlier, geologists would always find certain types of fossils associated with certain ages of rock. Again using our very simplified picture, let us suppose that in rocks types *ABCD* no fossils are ever found, then in rock types *E* and *F*, simple organisms occur (let's call them *ef*). In *GH* more complex organisms (*gh*), *IJK* even more complex animals (*ijk*) and so on up to the most recent *Z* (*z*). Fossils from later rocks *ijk* never occur in earlier rocks *EF*, but some fossils from *EF* (*ef*) might occur even in rock types *XYZ*.

It is important to understand that the relative dating of the rocks *A...Z* is independent of the fossils *e...z*. However, the fossils become a very useful tool to independently point to the date of the rocks and are often used for that purpose.

A couple of important points here: firstly, that the establishment of the geological column was never straightforward: plenty of arguments and reassessments went on as new information required it to be corrected. Secondly, from time to time geologists might come across a sequence which had the order *NMLKJ*. Did this mean that the column was wrong about the relative dating? No. What the geologist would then do is to look at the surrounding geology and in such a case would look for signs that the rock sequence had been physically turned on its head by earthquake etc., which would account for the reversal.

I spoke about relative dating. Type *A* is older than type *R*, but how much older was more difficult to assess in the 19th century. One method was to use uniformitarianism. Behind this rather long word are a number of practical, common sense principles. By no means infallible, but useful as long as the limitations of the idea are born in mind.

1. The laws of nature are constant: so gravity, fluid dynamics (how water flows), erosion, glaciation etc. worked in the past as they can be observed working today.
2. From modern observations and measurements of these phenomena estimates can be made about how long features in the past, such as deposition of sedimentary rocks, took to form.
3. Its limitations were that climate in the past was an unknown quantity—thus, how much rain fell would of course affect how quickly valleys were eroded, sediments deposited and so forth.

Using these principles, and bearing in mind their limitations, geologists estimated that the earth was certainly several hundred million years old.

Interestingly, this presented the world of science with a problem just as it did to the interpretation of the Bible.

The problem for science lay, not on earth, but in the sun. There was much acknowledged ignorance about how the sun functioned. At first it had been thought that its energy had to come from chemical reactions, some kind of combustion, but then it could only have burned for a few hundred years. Then the famous physicist Lord Kelvin (from whom we get the Absolute Temperature scale in 'Kelvin' or K) produced the theory that the heat came from the compression of gas under gravity but even then he calculated that it would only last a few million years and he remained convinced therefore that the geological calculations were mistaken and rejected Darwinism primarily for that reason—he did not think there was enough time for Darwin's theory to work.

"Expect the unexpected" needs to be graven on every scientist's desk! What Lord Kelvin could not anticipate was the discovery that the sun is fuelled by *nuclear* fusion reactions. It has nuclear fuel enough for billions of years. To be fair to him, he was right about the compression of gas under gravity causing heat: what he did not realise was that the heat generated would eventually lead to the ignition of nuclear fusion reactions.

In fact the 19th century geologists had considerably under-estimated how old the earth is. The modern figure puts it at around four and a half *billion* years old.

The approximate age of the earth as worked out by geology really is proven beyond all reasonable doubt. This is what I meant earlier when I said that to attack Darwinism on this front is hopeless. But remember the age of the earth and Darwinism are separate. It is quite true that an ancient earth would appear to support Darwinism, but then Darwinism is riding on the back of this evidence like a parasite using its host. The host is not the parasite. Sometimes enemy submarines can sneak into harbours under the shadow of a friendly ship and wreak havoc. Just so Darwinism has sneaked its ideas in under the 'protection' of a genuinely ancient earth.

Look at it like a detective story where it appears as if the evidence against our hero is sufficient to convict him. I hope to show that the evidence of an ancient earth is not proof against creation and that despite the evidence Darwinism will not get away with the 'crime'. But we must use "the little grey cells"! We will set about this later on in ch. 9.

If we accept for the moment that the earth is ancient, then there is one very fundamental issue that needs to be addressed: death before the Fall. Probably this single issue, which is of enormous importance, is the other plank in the Young Earth approach. If death came about as a result of the Fall, then clearly long ages of Succession of species being created, living, dying and many species becoming extinct is not an option. At first sight the Bible would seem to challenge the ancient earth idea.

Overview of the Geological Column		
Millions of years	Period or Epoch	ERA
	Pleistocene	CAENOZOIC
1.8	Pliocene	
5	Miocene	
25	Oligocene	
38	Eocene	
55	Palaeocene	
65		
	Cretaceous	MESOZOIC
144	Jurassic	
213	Triassic	
248	Permian	PALAEOZOIC
286	Carboniferous	
354	Devonian	
412	Silurian	
435	Ordovician	
492	Cambrian	
570		
Millions of years	Precambrian	

Death be not proud, *though some have called thee*

Mighty and dreadful, for thou art not so,

For those, whom thou think'st thou dost overthrow,

Die not, poor death, nor yet canst thou kill me.

From rest and sleep, which but thy pictures be,

Much pleasure, then from thee, much more must flow,

And soonest our best men with thee do go,

Rest of their bones, and souls' delivery.

Thou art slave to Fate, Chance, kings, and desperate men,

And dost with poison, war, and sickness dwell,

And poppy or charms can make us sleep as well,

And better than thy stroke; why swell'st thou then?

One short sleep past, we wake eternally,

And death shall be no more, death, thou shalt die.

John Donne
1572-1631

Chapter 5

Death before the Fall

Therefore, just as sin entered the world through one man, and death through sin, and in this way death came to all men, because all sinned—for before the law was given, sin was in the world. But sin is not taken into account when there is no law.

Nevertheless, death reigned from the time of Adam to the time of Moses, even over those who did not sin by breaking a command, as did Adam, who was a pattern of the one to come.

Rom 5:12-14

In interpreting this passage the plain meaning would be that Adam's sin brought death, not just to Adam but to the world. However, at the risk of appearing pedantic, Paul says that death (because of sin) came to all *men* (humans), not necessarily to all creatures.

Let us see where this leads. If, as Young Creationists argue, each Day is 24 hours and that therefore the consequence of eating the fruit was death that very day (ie 24 hr period) we must conclude that the death being referred to is *spiritual* death—separation from fellowship with God—but not physical death, for that did not occur for Adam for over 900 years. Spiritual death is not an option for animals—they are not like us: body, soul and spirit.

What can be drawn from this is the possibility that physical dying—the ceasing of biological function—could have pre-existed the Fall of man. There are a number of pointers in Genesis which support this.

1. Plants

11 Then God said, "Let the land produce vegetation: seed-bearing plants and trees on the land that bear fruit with seed in it, according to their various kinds." And it was so. Gen 1:11

Now seeds imply reproduction, and reproduction, by definition, implies offspring to replace dying vegetation—necessary, after all, if animals were to eat it. Are we to suppose that not a single blade of grass ever perished before the Fall?

Jesus says in John 12:24,

24 I tell you the truth, unless a grain of wheat falls to the ground and dies, it remains only a single seed. But if it dies, it produces many seeds.

This implies death of some kind at least amongst the vegetable kingdom.

If there was mature creation of the planet, was the earth created fully supplied with vegetation? If so, what are we to make of Gen 1:22 suggesting the need to spread?

God blessed them and said, "Be fruitful and increase in number and fill the water in the seas, and let the birds increase on the earth."

2. Meaning

'In the Day you eat of it you will die.'

If Adam had never seen physical death what would this statement have meant to him? A word must have a context to have meaning. However, if the phenomenon of animal death was already in existence, it would make good sense.

3. The Tree of Life

From the statement of God in Gen 3:22:

22 And the LORD God said, "The man has now become like one of us, knowing good and evil. He must not be allowed to reach out his hand and take also from the tree of life and eat, and live for ever."

The purpose of this Tree was to give Adam eternal life, implying that he did not have eternal life when he was created. He must therefore have been created mortal with only the *potential* for immortality.

In some way physical death would have to be understood as, in itself, not an evil at all prior to the Fall, but rather the spiritual principle at work—dying that we might more fully live. Adam was not immortal prior to his disobedience: otherwise what is the sense of driving him out of the garden, "lest he eat of the tree of life and live for ever"? Maybe, had he not fallen, eating of the tree of life would have given him the "power to lay down his life and the power to take it again (in the eternal realm)" as Jesus said:

17 "For this reason the Father loves Me, because I lay down My life so that I may take it again.

18 "No one has taken it away from Me, but I lay it down on My own initiative. I have authority to lay it down, and I have authority to take it up again. This commandment I received from My Father."

John 10:17–18

We look in vain for the Bible to answer the question, "What would have happened if Adam had not disobeyed?", but maybe the phrase "flesh and blood cannot inherit the Kingdom of God" is true on more than one level:

(i) on the level of the phrase being equivalent to our sinful natures,

(ii) on the level that there is a real physical impossibility of entering into eternity "with our old skins on". Paul says we need new bodies in the resurrection (1 Cor 15).

From this I would suggest that the Scriptures are not in contradiction to the idea of an ancient earth, nor in contradiction to the evidence for the Succession of species or the existence of *physical* death before the Fall.

The Day in Genesis Chs.1-3

Young Creationists place extreme emphasis on the 24 hour nature of the Day in Genesis 1. In Hebrew '*yom*' means day. That is its prime and plain meaning. Is there any evidence that the Bible uses it in any other way or sense?

A verse often used is that in Ps 90:4 NASB

For a thousand years in Thy sight
Are like yesterday when it passes by,
Or as a watch in the night.

It has been argued exegetically that the Millennium figure of the 1000 year reign of Christ on earth is allied to the Old Testament prophecies of 'The Day of the Lord' = 1000 earth years.

A Jewish exegesis of Genesis Ch.1 was that each Day was 1000 years and creation took 6000 years!

Peter uses this verse in 2 Peter 3:8. He has other purposes, but it does imply in passing that God's time and ours are very different.

Then we come to Gen Ch.2:4

These are the generations of the heavens and of the earth when they were created, in the day [yom] that the LORD God made the earth and the heavens.

Note here the use of Day. This verse summarises the creation in Chapter 1, yet refers to the six Days as 'the Day' (*yom*). Clearly the Bible is not restricting the meaning of *yom* to a 24 hour period.

Gen 2:16-17 KJV

16 And the LORD God commanded the man, saying, Of every tree of the garden thou mayest freely eat:

17 But of the tree of the knowledge of good and evil, thou shalt not eat of it: for in the day that thou eatest of it thou shalt surely die.

Once again, the word in v.17 is Day [yom]. Now this passage is double-edged. In one sense the immediate consequence of Adam eating the fruit was spiritual death, but his physical death was not for some 900 years! So arguably here the word Day means 900 years or so—possibly a shortfall from the 1000 years of the millennial age.

In Daniel (Dan 9:24–26 NASB):

24 "Seventy weeks have been decreed for your people and your holy city, to finish the transgression, to make an end of sin, to make atonement for iniquity, to bring in everlasting righteousness, to seal up vision and prophecy and to anoint the most holy place.

25 "So you are to know and discern that from the issuing of a decree to restore and rebuild Jerusalem until Messiah the Prince there will be seven weeks and sixty-two weeks; it will be built again, with plaza and moat, even in times of distress.

26 "Then after the sixty-two weeks the Messiah will be cut off and have nothing, and the people of the prince who is to come will destroy the city and the sanctuary. And its end will come with a flood; even to the end there will be war; desolations are determined."

Here we are required to interpret this to mean 70 × 7 = 490 years, making a day = one year.

From the Greater to the Lesser: the Sabbath commandment

For in six days the LORD made the heavens and the earth, the sea, and all that is in them, but he rested on the seventh day. Therefore the LORD blessed the Sabbath day and made it holy.

Exodus 20:11

In Scripture the greater to the lesser contrast or association is made.

Thus Gen 1: man is created *in the image of God*—but this is a greater to the lesser. We are not God, but we have small finite attributes of God—consciousness, creativity, fellowship in spirit etc.—marred by the Fall, of course.

Thus in the New Testament Eph 3:14-15:

[14 For this reason I kneel before the Father,] 15 from whom his whole family in heaven and on earth derives its name.

ἐξ οὗ πᾶσα πατριὰ ἐν οὐρανοῖς καὶ ἐπὶ γῆς ὀνομάζεται,

literally: 'from which all fatherhood in heaven and on earth is named.'

Here again we see the greater to the lesser: God's Fatherhood and human fatherhood.

It is perfectly reasonable therefore that the use of Day could have a similar 'greater to lesser' implication as in the passage in Exodus 20:8-11:

8 Remember the Sabbath day by keeping it holy.

9 Six days you shall labour and do all your work,

10 but the seventh day is a Sabbath to the LORD your God. On it you shall not do any work, neither you, nor your son or daughter, nor your manservant or maidservant, nor your animals, nor the alien within your gates.

11 For in six days the LORD made the heavens and the earth, the sea, and all that is in them, but he rested on the seventh day. Therefore the LORD blessed the Sabbath day and made it holy.

For God: seven great Ages; for man: seven 24 hour periods. Indeed the implication of Gen 2:2 is that we are still in the Seventh Day—for unlike the other six days it does not conclude with the 'evening and morning...' formula—and Scripture states that a sabbath still remains for the people of God:

8 For if Joshua had given them rest, God would not have spoken later about another day.

9 There remains, then, a Sabbath-rest for the people of God;

10 for anyone who enters God's rest also rests from his own work, just as God did from his.

Heb 4:8-10

Thus we can see that Scripture, even in Gen Ch1.ff, does not restrict the meaning of Day to the 'plain meaning' interpretation.

Chapter 6

We need to do some more spade work

1. Scientific truth is always provisional. Facts generally remain facts, but interpretation of those facts—the area of theory—is inevitably partial, frequently flawed and should always be open to being tested to destruction.

2. Bible Truth is never provisional, unless specifically stated to be so (eg Matthew 19:8). However, our interpretation is often provisional and flawed. We ought not to guard our interpretations of the Bible from hard criticism by claiming that they are what the Bible means. We could be in danger of being presumptuous. Of course, we can rightly defend our understanding vigorously, but we must not dismiss another's arguments by claiming that their view denies the authority of Scripture, tempting though that can be, unless that claim can be demonstrated by proper argument!

The interpretation of Scripture

Above all, you must understand that no prophecy of Scripture came about by the prophet's own interpretation. For prophecy never had its origin in the will of man, but men spoke from God as they were carried along by the Holy Spirit.

2 Peter 1:20-21

We often bring to the debate our own rules of interpretation, which, though doubtless sensible in many ways, are nonetheless our rules, not what Scripture says.

Thus many say that the first rule is that the plain meaning of the words of Scripture are the actual meaning unless good grounds can be found to think otherwise (eg metaphor in poetic passages etc.) and often a corollary is added to the effect that no further or alternative meaning should be sought.

Now this was the basis of the Reformers' attack on the Catholic Magisterium's interpretations of Scripture, so it has an honourable tradition, but it is often forgotten that its common sense origin was in the Humanist teachings of people like Erasmus (this is not secular humanism).

Poetry and Prose

It is often argued by supporters of the Young Earth Theory that Ancient creationists say that Genesis ch.1 is poetic and therefore need not be taken literally. They rightly point out that Genesis 1 is not written as poetry but as prose. Further, the distinction itself is no let out anyway. The plain meanings in the Psalms and the Prophets would count for nothing if this distinction was over-used! Thus Ancient creationists cannot simply hide behind the screen of poetry to maintain their position.

But how does Scripture use Scripture? A huge topic, but I'm going to use one difficult example.

14 So he got up, took the child and his mother during the night and left for Egypt,

15 where he stayed until the death of Herod. And so was fulfilled what the Lord had said through the prophet: "Out of Egypt I called my son."

Mt 2:14-15

This is a quotation from Hosea 11:1-3:

1 When Israel was a child, I loved him, and out of Egypt I called my son.

2 But the more I called Israel, the further they went from me. They sacrificed to the Baals and they burned incense to images.

3 It was I who taught Ephraim to walk, taking them by the arms; but they did not realise it was I who healed them.

What is clear is that Matthew is not using the 'plain meaning of scripture' here. Something more subtle is going on. Behind Matthew's use lies a Midrashic understanding of Scripture. Matthew is describing pattern and fulfilment: Abraham comes out of Egypt; Joseph's body comes out of Egypt; then Israel comes out of Egypt; then the Messiah comes out of Egypt: pattern and fulfilment.

The Reformers used the plain meaning to cut through the allegorical complexities of Medieval theology and did so to our great gain, but we have a baby and bathwater here. The cure for misuse is not necessarily disuse, but proper use. A useful tool (plain meaning) became nearly the only tool allowed. A spanner is useful but it cannot act as a screwdriver.

How does the Bible describe natural phenomena?

Does it describe natural phenomena as a scientist would try to do? In other words, does it describe, not just the outward appearance, but its inner mechanisms?

The simplest example can be used. The Bible speaks in many passages about the sun rising and setting, both in poetic passages and in narrative passages. Is this to be taken as a scientific statement? I believe we would all agree that it is not.

In three passages the Bible states (1 Chron 16:30, Ps 93:1, Ps 96:10): "The world is firmly established; it cannot be moved." Is this a scientific statement? Again we would all agree that it is not. But note that here too we must not hide behind poetry—we cannot arbitrarily decide that this is poetic and another passage is not.

The Bible itself describes the careful study of nature:

32 He [Solomon] *spoke three thousand proverbs and his songs numbered a thousand and five.*

33 He described plant life, from the cedar of Lebanon to the hyssop that grows out of walls. He also taught about animals and birds, reptiles and fish.

34 Men of all nations came to listen to Solomon's wisdom, sent by all the kings of the world, who had heard of his wisdom.

1 Kings 4:32-34

But v33 is not expanded on. God's Word contains some of Solomon's proverbs (Book of Proverbs) and wisdom (Ecclesiastes), some of which bear traces of his botanical and zoological studies as parables, but the studies themselves are not seen as being very relevant to the central message of the Word of God (not that they were without interest, of course).

In the above two examples the Bible describes natural phenomena in a simple 'appearance' manner. It is WYSIWYG (what you see is what you get), if you like. It is not primarily interested in discussing the mechanism behind the appearance. Knowing, as we do, that the earth circles the sun and revolves on its own axis every 24 hours actually makes little difference to our daily lives: we enjoy day and night, we walk out of our front doors without feeling giddy at the fact that the ground beneath our feet is travelling at a rotational speed of up to 1000mph (depending on latitude) and a speed round the sun of nearly 67,000mph. And around the galaxy at 140,000mph and that the galaxy is moving relative to the universe at a staggering 1,350,000mph. These facts are interesting but not central to our lives. We do not change our plans for the day because of them—unless, of course, we are planning a trip to the moon!

The lesson I would draw first of all is that until the time of Copernicus and Galileo, and for a while after, most Christians believed the earth was fixed and the sun went round it, based on what the Bible supposedly said about astronomy. However, I think few would hold to that position today. The passages that our forebears would insist were unequivocal (see Luther's comment on page 14) about the matter, we would not regard as a scientific statement about the solar system. Such a shift in position brings with it both 'a blessing and a curse'!

It frees us to examine nature in a less constrained way. We don't bring to a particular phenomenon a preconceived idea of how it must work. This is good as long as we remember the point at the beginning of this chapter about the nature of science.

The curse lies in the fact that fallen man finds it hard to keep an unbiased mind-set about a phenomenon. He often mistakes the explanation of *how* something works with the more fundamental question of *why* it works. He spends too much time trying to wrench science from its connection with the Creator of all things.

Can we then take the above principles and apply them straightforwardly to Genesis? It's not that simple.

Genesis 1-2 has Creation as its central theme, whereas the other passages touch on the sun or the earth in a more incidental way.

The Young Earth theory takes the plain meaning approach—which is biblically legitimate, of course, but not necessarily the only approach.

They therefore bring their 'plain meaning' of Genesis 1-2 as the basis to interpret scientific data. Remember that this plain meaning methodology has its origin in the Reformers' use of Humanistic interpretation of Scripture. To fill this out: Humanists like Erasmus taught that interpreting Scripture was no different from interpreting any other text and therefore we use our human reason to understand it (hence the name, Humanism), as we would to any other book. The possible dangers hidden in this approach become apparent: ordinary human reasoning (whether by a believer or non-believer) is the basis of the 'plain meaning' interpretation of Scripture; then, from this interpretation, human reasoning, based on the results of plain meaning understanding of the Bible, is brought to bear on scientific data. This process generates some very difficult problems both in understanding Scripture and in interpreting scientific data as we have already seen.

The fact that scientific truths are always provisional and Biblical Truth is eternal does not imply that the latter is designed to inform the former: if it did, strangely, Biblical Truth could lose its eternal verity. Think! If a Bible truth today appears to agree with a particular piece of scientific truth today, then what happens when, as it very likely must, the scientific truth of today becomes the scientific mistake of yesterday? Could not that bring down the eternal verity of the Bible? It was perilously close to doing that at the time of Galileo.

It is instructive to see what happened then. The Church had been heavily Hellenised—that is, it had allowed Greek philosophy to dictate the basis for understanding the Bible. Influences came from Plato, Aristotle, in both 'theology' and natural philosophy (what we might very loosely call science). In astronomy the key figure was Ptolemy of Alexandria, who wrote the *Almagest* in about 150AD.

The Ptolmaic model of the Universe was earth centred, so it seemed to agree with the Bible or, rather, the Bible seemed to agree with *it*. The model was a remarkable achievement—it was uncannily accurate and accounted very well for the strange movements of the planets (wanderers, as the Greek name implied) by the sophisticated use of epicycles (circles within circles) for their 'orbits'.*

> * Ptolemy did have a grasp of the size of the earth compared to the universe: "The earth in relation to the fixed stars has no size and must be regarded as a mathematical point."

When Copernicus and Galileo resurrected another more ancient Greek idea that the solar system was heliocentric (Aristarchus of Samos *c.*310-230BC) they were of course laughed at and worse. Not least because their model was initially less accurate than Ptolemy's. It took Kepler, Newton and others to resolve the initial difficulties presented by Copernicus' model. But his model was basically correct,
1. because it was based on observations.
2. Occam's razor: that one should not multiply hypotheses, or in a modern idiomatic form: K.I.S.S. = Keep It Simple, Stupid!

By trying to hook Greek philosophical ideas to the Bible, the Bible was in danger of seeming to be found wanting when the philosophy behind the church's interpretation was overturned. Remember that this resistance to the new astronomy was as strong in the Protestant Churches as it was in Catholicism!

The lesson we need to draw from this is that it can be dangerous to insist on a particular scientific interpretation of Genesis, because when the science fails it may look as if the Bible has failed.

Today, Young Earth theorists have to accept that the earth goes round the sun despite the fact that the Bible suggests that the earth does not move. But, for example, are they committed to the following 'science'?

22 The eye is the lamp of the body. If your eyes are good, your whole body will be full of light.

23 But if your eyes are bad, your whole body will be full of darkness. If then the light within you is darkness, how great is that darkness!

Mt 6:22-23

34 Your eye is the lamp of your body. When your eyes are good, your whole body also is full of light. But when they are bad, your body also is full of darkness.

35 See to it, then, that the light within you is not darkness.

36 Therefore, if your whole body is full of light, and no part of it dark, it will be completely lighted, as when the light of a lamp shines on you."

Lk 11:34-36

Behind these two teachings of Jesus lies the understanding that the ancient world had about how sight worked. They believed that the eyes produced a kind of ray which scanned the world around them and thereby enabled sight to work. Not a very consistent theory, of course. But are Christians thereby committed to this theory because Jesus used the idea? I think not.

But we must leave behind now the rather cramped and claustrophobic cosmos of the Young Earth Theory and begin to see just how amazing our Creator God is.

Ascertainable truth is piecemeal, partial, uncertain, and difficult.
Bertrand Russell

Part II
Cosmology

Chapter 7

A brief history of scientific ideas

As stated earlier, it is often assumed that an old earth is something invented by Evolutionists to support their theory. Darwin needed vast amounts of time for his theory to work; therefore geologists tried to show that the earth was very old.

However, the reverse is actually the case. Geology had demonstrated for more than a century before Darwin that the earth could not reasonably be considered to be only 6000 years old, and by the mid 1800s was already estimated to be several hundreds of millions of years old. However, Darwin was in fact very worried that there still was not enough time for his gradual evolution. Even though recent study strongly suggests that the earth may be up to 4500 million years old, the period during which complex life burgeoned is still thought to be only several hundred million years. It is no way anything like approaching the kind of time needed for the most optimistic scenario for Evolution to occur 'by chance'.

Some of those geologists of the 19th century were themselves Bible-believing Christians. Adam Sedgwick in particular castigated Darwin's hypothesis—Sedgwick had been Darwin's Cambridge tutor. Hugh Miller, the Scottish geologist, was a strong Evangelical Christian and had no time for earlier versions of evolution (and there were quite a few), such as Robert Chambers' popular book, *Vestiges of the Natural History of Creation* (1844), though Miller did not quite live to read Darwin's theory. Had he done so, his critique would have been trenchant! Miller had, in his earlier years, briefly espoused the gap theory, put forward by the respected Scottish preacher, Revd Dr Thomas Chalmers, in 1805, but changed his view to the Day-age concept.

The Big Bang

Many do not realise that 'The Big Bang' was the name given to the theory by Sir Fred Hoyle as a term of abuse. Hoyle was an agnostic* who believed in the Steady State Theory—the idea that the Universe has always been here. For him, 'The Big Bang' suggested a beginning and therefore, worse, suggested a Beginner. In passing, though, it is worthy of note that Hoyle himself found the evolutionary theory about the origin of life quite unacceptable. His assistant, now professor, Chandra Wickramasinghe, demonstrated its statistical implausibility.

* However, Hoyle later wrote, "Would you not say to yourself, 'Some super-calculating intellect must have designed the properties of the carbon atom, otherwise the chance of my finding such an atom through the blind forces of nature would be utterly minuscule.' Of course you would" ... "A common sense interpretation of the facts suggests that a superintellect has monkeyed with physics, as well as with chemistry and biology, and that there are no blind forces worth speaking about in nature. The numbers one calculates from the facts seem to me so overwhelming as to put this conclusion almost beyond question." Hoyle, an atheist until that time, said that this suggestion of a guiding hand left him "greatly shaken."

Some preliminary points about interpretation of Genesis.
1. Only God, Father, Son and Holy Spirit, was present before and during Creation. Therefore the account in Scripture was given to Moses by God. It might have been handed down from Adam, but as God spoke to Moses 'face to face' it is more likely that it was direct revelation.
2. It would be clearly of no use to the people of Israel to be presented with a modern 'scientific' treatise on Creation. It must needs be presented in a way that they (as well as we) could understand.
3. We will bring to bear on Genesis the WYSIWYG nature of descriptions of natural phenomena used by the Bible in general.

66

4. Whatever view we hold on Creation, one thing that the Scriptures make clear is the greatness and awesome power of our Creator God whose existence is from all Eternity and who is described in Daniel as "The Ancient of Days". Metaphors to describe this awesome majesty and power in Scripture stretch human language to its very limit. There were no simple words in Hebrew to convey the vast magnitudes of time and space. Everything in Scripture on these themes points to language pushed to its limits and beyond.

This is very important in our understanding of Creation. Unwittingly, the Young Earth Theory would actually seem to reverse this sense of vastness, reducing the extent of both time and space. The Universe it proposes verges on the claustrophobic.

Let me sketch out what the current theories are about how the Universe began and developed.

In the beginning...

There is an immense explosion of energy from nowhere at temperatures that are unimaginably high. As it says in Heb 11:3 NASB:

By faith we understand that the worlds were prepared by the word of God, so that what is seen was not made out of things which are visible.

As this explosion expands it is like a bubble which is not only expanding energy but also expanding time and space (*This is what God the LORD says—he who created the heavens and stretched them out....* Isaiah 42:5). In the first few millionths of a second it begins to 'cool'. It is mostly photons (light), but as it cools energy starts condensing into matter ($e=mc^2$) in the form of sub-atomic particles.

As time continues this temperature drops, so that after about 30 minutes the temperature has dropped to around 100,000,000°C. By this time atomic nuclei have begun to condense out; mostly hydrogen and a little helium.

Let us pause here briefly. Right from the start the expansion process was not precisely uniform, but slightly 'unbalanced'. This 'imbalance' tipped the process toward the production of more matter than anti-matter—if this had not happened the whole explosion would have just as suddenly reversed into nothing. Moving on. As the new Universe continued to expand the boundaries of time and space, matter continued to cool and to begin to clump together (again because of the imbalance) under the influence of gravitational forces.

Eventually (and we have moved on a long time) this matter condensed into huge clouds which formed into stars and galaxies of stars. These first stars are fuelled by nuclear fusion of hydrogen and helium. The fusion process generates heavier elements which eventually cause the star to explode showering these heavier elements into space then to condense into second generation stars and, in our case, a solar system of planets.

I am certain any physicist or astronomer reading this account would wince at the crudity of my descriptions, but I'm trying just to give a brief overview.

What evidence is there for any of this?

1. The Universe is expanding still and this can be observed occurring. If it is expanding, then by reversing time it is reasonable to deduce that it must have started from a single point.
2. There is good evidence of what might be called the 'echo' of the big bang which can be monitored today—sometimes known as the 3°K background microwave radiation: the initial shock wave attenuated over billions of years.
3. The imbalance, or 'ripples', in the original expansion have also been measured in this 'echo' by the COBE satellite.

The further into space we look, the further back in time we look. So, up to a point, we can look back through the unfolding of the Universe in real life. A telescope is also a time machine. Just recently it was announced that the radiation from the first generation stars has been detected—the stars themselves cannot be seen; they are still 'over the horizon'.

Just how old is all this? Well, here it depends on the theory to some extent. The current view is that the Universe is around 13,700 million years old, the formation of the earth being some 4,500 million years ago. These figures are not written in stone; they may be wrong, but they are most unlikely to be so wrong as to suggest a 6000 year old sun, moon and earth.

Before anyone jumps to a conclusion that the picture I've drawn of the formation of the Universe looks 'random' or mere chance, the whole thing is so finely tuned (in terms of repulsive and attractive forces) that were it to have been different by one part in a million million, there would have been no Universe!

So right from the beginning the evidence suggests that 'Someone' is in charge.

So what did God reveal to Moses? And how?

We know what he revealed, for it is recorded for us in Genesis. But how? This is speculative, because Genesis gives no particular clues, but it could have been by a succession of clear visions. Moses was shown the pattern of the Tabernacle in this way, it would seem:

This is how the lampstand was made: It was made of hammered gold—from its base to its blossoms. The lampstand was made exactly like the pattern [literally 'appearance'] *the LORD had shown Moses.*

Num 8:4

To use a somewhat trivial illustration, we might imagine Moses was shown a Powerpoint presentation of God's activity in Creation. Everything is described as if by an observer on the earth as it is formed and filled with life. If we allow that this description is WYSIWYG, ie with no particular intention to describe the hidden processes behind what is observed, then the stately progression of creation from the inorganic to organic and finally to the pinnacle of God's creation—the creation of humankind—bears an astonishing resemblance to what is called the Succession of species gleaned from the geological record. Each Day, each 'slide', highlighting the key feature or features of this Succession at its particular stage.

Remembering the WYSIWYG manner of presentation, the mystery of Light and Day and Night being apparently 'created' before the sun and moon (Day 4) can be resolved. Until the fourth Day the observer would have seen no stars in the sky as the atmosphere was totally cloudy (just a shifting brightness and darkness as the day and night progressed); only after the change of atmosphere, caused primarily by the photosynthesis of early chlorophyllic bacteria and subsequent plant life (Day 3), would the skies clear and the heavenly bodies be visible from earth.

What Moses is shown is an overview of creation, but not primarily for the purpose of scientific explanation, but for the purpose of revelation that God is God and he is the Creator of all things and that this God created human beings to delight in him (and, in passing, to blow away all the nonsense that the Israelites would have picked up in Egypt and in Canaan about polytheism and pagan myths). For all *false* religion has associated with it a false science—look at Hinduism as an instance. This point is well expressed by Hugh Miller in 1856:

Let us farther remark, that since it seems inevitable that pretended revelations of ancient date should pledge themselves to a false science, the presumption must be strong that an ancient revelation of great multiplicity of detail, which has not so pledged itself, is not a false, but a true revelation. Nay, if we find in it the line drawn between what man can know of himself and what he cannot know, and determine that this line was traced in a remote and primitive age, we have positive evidence in the circumstance, good so far as it extends, of its Divine origin. Now, it will be ultimately found that this line was drawn with exquisite precision in the Hebrew Scriptures,—not merely the most ancient works that profess to be revelations, but absolutely the most ancient of all writings. Unfortunately, however, what God seems to have done for His Revelation, influential theologians of both the Romish and orthodox Churches have laboured hard to undo; and, from their mistaking, in not a few remarkable passages, the scope and object of the vouchsafed message, they have at various times striven to pledge it to a science as false as even that of Buddhist, Teuton, or Hindu. And so, not only has the argument been weakened and obscured which might be founded on the rectitude of the line drawn of old between what ought and what ought not to be the subject of revelation, but even a positive argument has been furnished to the infidel,—ever ready to identify the glosses of the theologian with the enunciations of

Revelation itself,—similar to that which the Christian missionary directs against the false religions of India.

Testimony of the Rocks, 1856

His comment about those who 'labour to undo' what God has done in the Scriptures needs to be heeded today.

The discoverable and the revealed

Taking up Miller's most important point about Scripture, that it is not there to 'reveal' things that human beings can perfectly well find out for themselves, we need to labour this point. God has given us minds to use. We do not expect God to tell us the time in the morning when we pray or to tell us when to go to work or what to eat for lunch etc. These are obviously things we can do for ourselves. The pursuit of scientific enquiry is one of these areas. The Bible tells us nothing about electricity or steam engines, medicine or computers. Indeed, one could reasonably hazard the suggestion that Genesis deliberately does *not* give us the full picture of the Creation process partly because God intended human beings to have the joy and work of discovering such things for themselves. It is the dull and lazy student who looks for easy ways out of doing his assigned work—it is the good student who works hard to learn for himself. At school, some text books used to have the answers at the back of the book—but that only spoils it! These days, I suppose, this is one of the dangers of the internet.

I have already touched on the concept in Biblical interpretation gleaned from another remarkable 19th century writer, H. Grattan Guinness. He wrote *The Approaching End of the Age*. In it he gives an insightful interpretation of the books of Daniel and Revelation. Amongst a number of important conclusions he deduces the return of the people of Israel to the Land and gives a very remarkable estimate as to when that process would begin!

One of the major areas of his exposition is seeing the prophecies of Daniel and Revelation working out in the history of the Church. He argues that the prophecies require us (from this end of history) to use the information given us by 'profane' (ie secular) history to see how these prophecies have been and are being fulfilled since the New

Testament canon was closed. God gave the prophecies, but we need to apply our knowledge of subsequent history to understand how they are working out. He also uses the idea of 'progressive revelation': that is, that in the Bible we see God's purposes prophetically laid out, but they begin almost as hints (eg Gen 3:15) and bit by bit through the OT the germ of the Messianic Promise progressively gets filled out in more and more detail. He deduces from this that Revelation, being the last book of prophecy in the Bible, gives the fullest expression to the future history of the Church and Jesus's Return and the signs accompanying that return and the ushering in of the Millennium and after.

> GOD has been pleased to make three great revelations of Himself to man: his Works; his Word; and his Son, and these revelations have been progressive in character. Nature, the Law, the Gospel; a silent material universe, an inspired Book, a living God-man; these are the three great steps that have led from the death and darkness of sin to that knowledge of the true God which is eternal life. A fourth revelation of God, fuller and more perfect than any, is yet to come. The only begotten Son, who is in the bosom of the Father, who is the brightness of his glory and the express image of his person, who "declared Him" when He came the first time in grace and humiliation, will declare Him yet more fully when He comes a second time in righteousness and in glory. Then the earth will be filled with the knowledge of the Lord, as the waters cover the sea.
>
> H. Grattan Guinness, *The Approaching End of the Age* 1879

I would like to suggest that we may approach Genesis Ch.1 in a similar way. It is, in a sense, 'retrospective prophecy'. It was revealed directly and clearly to the prophet Moses, and written down under the inspiration of the Holy Spirit by him. It is about things which no human being could have known at the time, because they were not there. If we may, then it is perfectly proper to interpret Genesis, where appropriate, in the light of scientific discovery—just as other biblical prophecy is interpreted in the light of subsequent history not recorded as history in the Bible. Of course, we must realise the point made earlier about the provisional nature of scientific enquiry—the same being true of secular historical enquiry.

Chapter 8

Let there be Light!

IN the beginning God created the heavens and the earth.

2 The earth was formless and void, and darkness was over the surface of the deep, and the Spirit of God was moving over the surface of the waters.

3 Then God said, "Let there be light"; and there was light.

Gen 1:1-3 NASB

Just to recap on what we've already said.

v.1 is the headline or title. We noted that the heavens precede the earth and that tells us immediately that most of ch.1 is concerned almost entirely with the creation of planet Earth. The heavens are the backdrop of the main theme. That does not mean they are unimportant (later we will see just how important they are), but the main concern is about God, the Father, Son and Holy Spirit and his creation of the earth and of human kind and his relationship with them.

That is the centre of the whole chapter and subsequent chapters. What it may suggest about mechanism and process is secondary to this main purpose. This must be so as the description of process and mechanism is almost non-existent. It focuses on God's Word, "let there be..." and its result, "and it was so". How the Word was translated into result is not revealed. It may have been instantaneous, as the Young Earth Theory would require. It may have taken untold ages. The text leaves both open as possibilities. Can we decide, on a balance of probabilities, which is the more likely?

If we take the instantaneous view, this raises a question. Why, if each day's creativity is instantaneous, did not God make the whole thing come about instantaneously? Why spend days doing what could be instantaneous? This may not be an entirely fair question as ultimately God may do as he chooses, but it still needs to be considered.

On the long process side, what can be said?

Most of God's subsequent redemptive actions in history have been associated with long process.

God tells the serpent,

15 And I will put enmity
Between you and the woman,
And between your seed and her seed;
He shall bruise you on the head,
And you shall bruise him on the heel."

Gen 3:15 NASB

This is the first hint of God's redemptive plan, but it was to be some millennia before this would fully come to pass in Jesus the Messiah, the Son of God coming to redeem fallen humanity.

God has spoken the Word, and a long process (from our perspective) is set in motion.

Why could it not be done immediately? Not an easy question to answer, but it in fact looks as if Adam and Eve thought it would be!

I owe this point to Arnold Fruchtenbaum's *Messianic Christology,* which points out the very strange verse in Gen 4:1:

NOW the man had relations with his wife Eve, and she conceived and gave birth to Cain, and she said, "I have gotten a manchild [with the help of] the LORD."

In the Hebrew "with the help of" is not there. Literally it reads, "I have gotten a manchild: YAHWEH [the LORD]."

The similar Hebrew construction is in the following verse,

Again, she gave birth to his brother: Abel.

Eve thinks that her first child is the Redeemer, Yahweh made flesh!

Maybe there is an important lesson here. We as human beings are very impatient—we want it and we want it now, even good things, like the coming of the Messiah. Eve is right in thinking that the Redeemer will be God made flesh, but wrong about when this will occur.

So it is reasonable to propose that between the Word, "Let there

74

be..." and the outcome, "and it was so". could lie long processes which the text passes over as not being relevant to the central message. But why? Let us remind ourselves of the comment of Hugh Miller quoted above:

> Let us farther remark, that since it seems inevitable that pretended revelations of ancient date should pledge themselves to a false science, the presumption must be strong that an ancient revelation of great multiplicity of detail, which has not so pledged itself, is not a false, but a true revelation. Nay, if we find in it the line drawn between *what man can know of himself and what he cannot know*, and determine that this line was traced in a remote and primitive age, we have positive evidence in the circumstance, good so far as it extends, of its Divine origin. Now, it will be ultimately found that this line was drawn with exquisite precision in the Hebrew Scriptures,—not merely the most ancient works that profess to be revelations, but absolutely the most ancient of all writings.

"...what man can know of himself and what he cannot know,..."

This is the key to the question. God intends that human beings should study his works. Science is one of the gifts he gives us to use.

Great are the works of the LORD; They are studied by all who delight in them.

Psalm 111:2

These works are both his creation and his Law, as Psalm 19 makes clear:

> *THE heavens are telling of the glory of God;*
> *And their expanse is declaring the work of His hands.*
> *2 Day to day pours forth speech,*
> *And night to night reveals knowledge...*
> *...7 The law of the LORD is perfect, restoring the soul;*
> *The testimony of the LORD is sure, making wise the simple.*

His Law, his Word, his Truth needs to be revealed to us—we cannot work it out for ourselves—but his creative works are on display for all to see and to investigate. Adam was called to name the creatures, Solomon was a man who studied nature. The Bible's main purpose is to reveal God's Truth for salvation, not to tell us things we can find out for ourselves. It tells us, "How to go to heaven, not how the heavens go", as Galileo was reputed to have said.

So let us see where scientific knowledge about Creation is at the present time.

Fifty years ago, to study the early universe was considered by many as more or less 'off-limits' for physics. It was seen more as a matter of philosophy than of science. In so far as there was any theory, it was that the universe was infinite and has always been here. This was called the Steady State Theory and was proposed in the 1940s by Herman Bondi and Thomas Gold, with variations by Fred Hoyle. This theory conveniently disposed of the idea of any creation and for some seemed sufficient 'proof' to dispose of a creator as well! Its central idea was that, although the universe was expanding, matter came into existence between the galaxies to replace the matter being turned into energy by the nuclear furnaces of the stars: this matter/energy exchange was exactly balanced—hence the universe was in steady state.

Three bits of scientific knowledge were enough to raise serious doubts about this idea.

1. **A calculation:** if the universe is infinite in extent (both in space and time), with galaxies and stars randomly distributed (scattered like seeds over an infinite field) to infinity, then it was a relatively simple calculation to make as to how much light would be received by any point in the universe (such as the earth, for example) from the sum total of all the light from these stars. The calculation showed that if the above assumptions were correct then the night sky should be as bright as daylight! This most clearly is not so; therefore at least one of the assumptions above is incorrect! Either the Universe is not infinite or the stars are not randomly distributed to infinity both in terms of time and space: or both are not true. It looked as if the universe could not have existed always.

2. In terms of human life span, the stars seem to us unchanging. The ancients, of course, knew there were exceptions to this rule: comets and the planets (or wanderers as the Greeks called

them). Five were observable to the naked eye: Mercury, Venus, Mars, Jupiter and Saturn. When the telescope was invented in the 16th century, it was discovered that some of these planets had moons like the earth (Jupiter and Saturn) and that Saturn has a ring. In 1781 another planet was discovered by the astronomer Herschel: Uranus. But in 1718 Edmond Halley announced that he had observed that stars moved relative to each other. The 'fixed' heavens were not fixed.

Edwin Hubble in 1929 announced that the red shift*

* **Red Shift:** From the middle of the 19th century the visible spectrum of stars was being carefully noted. Spectra from stars and galaxies can tell us very clearly which particular elements are present by very precise black lines in the rainbow spectrum: they are like fingerprints for a chemical element. In many stars the main constituents are hydrogen and helium. Hydrogen has five specific absorption lines in the visible spectrum (see the picture on the back cover). Hubble and others had observed that stars clearly had the hydrogen fingerprint but that the set of lines had moved together towards the Red end of the spectrum—hence the term Red Shift. The explanation was remarkably simple. We have all experienced the Doppler effect: eg when a police or ambulance siren passes us, we hear the sound higher than it really is as it approaches and lower than it is as it heads away. It is similar with light. If the star or galaxy being observed were moving towards us then the spectrum of hydrogen would move towards the blue end of the spectrum; if away from us, then toward the red end. The latter is always what is observed. Therefore the galaxies are all moving away from us.

measurements of galaxies showed that every part of the universe is moving away from every other part; the further away from us a part is, the faster it is travelling relative to us. Although the Steady State Theory came later it had difficulty with this observation. Put another way, Hubble's discovery very strongly suggested that the Universe was flying apart as fragments of an explosion fly away from the central 'bang' in all directions. It is not quite as crude as that because the expansion is not going on in space, as an earthly explosion would do, but is the expansion of space-time itself taking the stars and galaxies with it. A frequently used analogy is to imagine a new balloon, as yet uninflated, on which you mark with a black pen little dots to represents stars or galaxies. Then the balloon is inflated. As the balloon gets bigger the dots on the skin move away from each other. Space-time expands and the objects in it move away from each other.

This provoked others into challenging the Steady State Theory with an alternative idea of a universe which began with a huge burst of energy. Fred Hoyle, the grand old man of the Steady State universe, ridiculed the theory as 'The Big Bang'. But the name has stuck.

3. Background microwave radiation.
Since the development of radio and radio astronomy, scientists had been puzzled by a background hiss to all radio signals in the microwave part of the spectrum. In 1964, two radio engineers, Arno Penzias and Robert Wilson, were working on some highly sensitive telephone radio equipment where they found this annoying hiss interfering with the signals. They tried everything to eliminate the source of the noise: local power lines, passing vehicles, even cleaning out bird droppings in the antennae! Still it persisted. It made no difference which direction the antennae pointed day or night. They made enquiries and discovered that the signal hiss was exactly the frequency and type predicted by the 'Big Bang' Theory for the existence of an 'echo' of the initial explosion attenuated in time and space to be a background radiation temperature of 3K which would generate the microwave hiss.

In 1990 the COBE (COsmic Background Explorer) satellite confirmed the radiation and mapped the slight fluctuations in its intensity which further strengthened the 'Big Bang' theory.

Scientists, theoretical and experimental, began to put together a description of what probably took place from within a few milliseconds of the initial 'explosion' of energy.

Time	Temperature in K*	Content
0	∞K ?	The 'Big Bang'
10 millisecs	100,000,000,000K	Photons†, electrons, positrons, neutrinos in an incredibly dense 'soup'
100 millisecs	30,000,000,000K	
3 minutes	1,000,000,000K	Add protons and neutrons, forming hydrogen and helium nuclei
400,000 years	3000K	Atoms form from nuclei and electrons. Gravity begins to clump these atoms into clouds
From a few million years		Galaxies start to form
9 billion years	a few degrees K	Our solar system forms
13.7 billion years	3K	Present day

* K is degree Kelvin. The scale interval is the same as Centigrade but 0 = Absolute Zero temperature, below which it is impossible to go (which is -273° on the Centigrade scale).
† Photons are the quantum particles we call Light.

The above must rank as one of the briefer 'histories of time'. The time spans, temperatures and processes are mind-bendingly awesome, but Genesis touches on this in even briefer words: 'In the beginning God created the heavens... And God said, "let there be light"'. For that is what the initial conditions contained—light, photons, enormous amounts contained in a tiny space. Without that Light nothing could happen that would bring about the earth. Remember that in vs.1-3 the earth 'was not there', it was 'without form and void'. From a cosmological perspective, billions of years would pass before the earth was formed, but Genesis immediately takes us to that formation. But can astronomy and physics fill in the gap? Yes it can. And it is well worth an excursion.

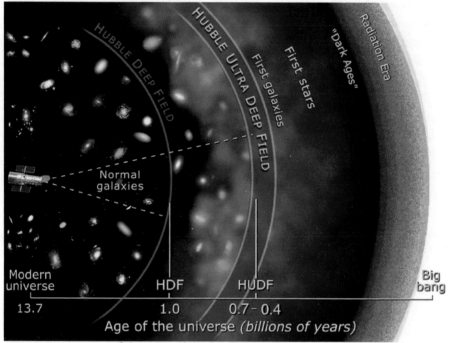

Schematic of the Big Bang to the present

The creation of stars

This began after the universe was perhaps a few million years old. The cooling matter, mostly hydrogen and some helium, is condensing under gravity into clouds and clumps; the clumps begin to shrink under gravitational pressures and as they shrink their temperature rises until the hydrogen nuclei start to fuse together and nuclear fusion begins and a star is born. Stars vary enormously in size. The general rule is: the larger the initial mass the hotter the star burns and, curiously, the shorter its life.

These are the first generation stars. When they 'die' they explode, often as supernovas, showering newly formed elements such as lithium, beryllium and carbon into the universe; these in turn become part of new star formations and the nuclear fusion process continues, generating heavier elements in the second generation stars, which in turn explode. The shock waves of the supernova explosions, as the debris flies away, generate further nuclear fusion reactions, creating the elements that are heavier than iron (the last element whose creation in a star generates energy). After a supernova explosion all that remains of the star is a 'collapsed matter' lump of neutrons, just a few hundred miles in diameter and incredibly dense, initially spinning at a rapid rate. These are the Pulsars that were discovered in the 1950s by radio astronomers: they flash their radio signals like the revolving beacon of a lighthouse. Such is their regularity that initially some suggested they were 'little green men' signalling to us! Sometimes a supernova of a massive star may generate an even more extreme object: a black hole. Another aspect to supernovas is that as well as the elements that spread into space there are tiny atomic fragments: protons, electrons and other particles which are broadcast, often at near the speed of light, throughout the galaxy and beyond. Later on in the book we will see just how important these particles, or cosmic rays, are to our own planet Earth.

Our sun is a second generation star, not too big and not too small, and able to burn for several billion years. Its death will not be a supernova, but as the fuel eventually runs out it will expand into a red giant (a bit like Betelgeuse—top left star in Orion—is today) and then finally collapse into a dark cinder.

As the dust cloud which was to become our Solar System gathered and condensed, it would begin to rotate, the sun's nuclear furnace ignited and the whirling remnants of the cloud in turn condensed into planetary objects: the inner ones containing a much higher proportion of the heavier elements. The outer planets are the 'gas giants', such as Jupiter, Saturn, Uranus and Neptune; beyond them may be a ring of debris, called the Kyper Belt, mostly ice, frozen methane etc. from which comets are formed and occasionally plunge inwards towards the sun in highly eccentric orbits.

The early period of the solar system would have been very exciting to watch! Collisions were frequent, the planets being bombarded with smaller bits of debris, rock and ice. Our own earth may have been struck, broken up and re-formed more than once in that early period—much of our water may have been brought in by comet-like projectiles from the outer edge of the solar system. This period is sometimes given the name the Hadean Period, for obvious reasons!

After about one billion years the earth is still hot but cooling and water is able to form oceans of some kind. The atmosphere may well have been water vapour (H_2O), methane (CH_4), nitrogen (N_2) and carbon dioxide (CO_2).

Then about three billion years ago an extraordinary change took place: 'simple' single-celled life forms were created. Some of these had a remarkable ability: they could use sunlight to convert CO_2 into oxygen (O_2). These still exist in parts of the world today and are called Stromatolites. It took perhaps another couple of billion years for the atmosphere to change. During this period another change took place. As these single celled creatures made oxygen, the oxygen reacted with the free iron on the earth's crust to produce iron ore—our planet literally rusted!

At some point toward the end of this period the temperature of the earth plummeted—and the planet froze nearly solid! Then about 600 million years ago it unfroze and the next most remarkable event took place: there was a sudden explosion of highly complex creatures almost from nowhere. It is referred to as the Cambrian Explosion—vegetation, sea creatures of many kinds emerged in an incredibly short space of geological time (this event, fully acknowledged by all scientists in the field, throws an enormous spanner into Darwinian Evolutionary theory, even in its most modified form). The body plans of most of the earth's species appeared at this time.

The climate continues to fluctuate with ice ages and super-warm periods, partly because the continental landmass breaks up and re-forms and drifts apart by the operation of plate tectonics.

300 million years ago: the earth is very warm and the land dominated by swamps and rainforest.

100 million years ago: the age of the dinosaurs, land, air and sea.

30 million years ago: mammals appear as dinosaurs are more or less wiped out, perhaps by a huge asteroid collision.

2 million years ago: hominid upright animals appear—not to be confused with true *Homo sapiens*.

From 50,000 years to perhaps around 6000 years ago: we are entering the era of Adam and Eve: the first actual human couple.

"A common sense interpretation of the facts suggests that a superintellect has monkeyed with physics, as well as with chemistry and biology, and that there are no blind forces worth speaking about in nature. The numbers one calculates from the facts seem to me so overwhelming as to put this conclusion almost beyond question."

Sir Fred Hoyle FRS

Chapter 9

Chance or Design?

Just look back over the brief outline in the last chapter. What strikes you? To me it is the patient preparation of the true Master Craftsman. For this planet to be suited for human habitation an enormous amount of preparation is required: first, the very elements that are needed ultimately to create life and a Universe big enough to produce them. Then, the forming of the sun and the solar system: so carefully designed that the sun is in just the right place in the galaxy—not too near the centre (where radiation levels would kill all life), not too far out where (strangely) the earth would risk getting too hot, the sun itself being just the right size—not too big, not too small, not too bright, not too dim, but sufficiently variable to allow for the creative acts of God to be transmitted into the material of the life on earth (a point to which we shall return).

But how did the Creator bring all this about? We know he did bring it about, because he revealed this to Moses in Genesis Chs. 1 & 2. But human beings are given intelligence and curiosity to look into the 'how?' for themselves.

This is important and often overlooked. To repeat Hugh Miller's comment again:

"Let us farther remark, that since it seems inevitable that pretended revelations of ancient date should pledge themselves to a false science, the presumption must be strong that an ancient revelation of great multiplicity of detail, which has not so pledged itself, is not a false, but a true revelation. Nay, if we find in it the line drawn between what man can know of himself and what he cannot know, and determine that this line was traced in a remote and primitive age, we have positive evidence in the circumstance... of its Divine origin. Now, it will be ultimately found that this line was drawn with exquisite precision in the Hebrew Scriptures..."

To be given all the answers would, if it does not sound too flippant, spoil it all. There is real fun, joy and achievement in discovering things for oneself; to "think God's thoughts after him" as Newton once put it; to be amazed at the subtlety and complexity of Creation, yet to discover the laws by which all things are governed.

Now if we are free to investigate, we are also free to make mistakes. Scientific endeavour has been a long history of mistakes, revisions and revolutions in understanding how the Universe works and how it came to be. But usually the general trend, for all the many false turns and blind alleys, is towards a clearer picture. But it is unlikely that we are ever going to arrive at the whole picture. Human beings cling too much to cherished theories, reluctant to let them go and to look afresh at evidence and experimental results. One current interest in the area of theoretical physics and cosmology is to put together a Theory Of Everything (abbreviated to TOE) integrating the physics of the huge with that of the minute quantum world. Well, good luck to them; no harm in giving it a go.

But there are areas of science which seem literally stuck in a bygone age: the area of theory in biology and, in particular, the theory of Evolution.

Darwin's theory of Evolution was first published in 1859 in *On the Origin of Species.*

What was the evidence that he based his theory on?

1. The fossil record gave a picture of Succession of Species from simple single-celled organisms to mammals and *homo sapiens.*

2. He observed that within a family of creatures, eg Galapagos finches (which he actually could make little of) and mocking birds, they could vary in behaviour, habitat, beak shape and plumage etc., each variety seeming to be most adapted to its habitat. He deduced that this suitability for a habitat would come about by selection of the fittest variation: they would survive better and therefore successfully breed, passing on the useful variation. This is Natural Selection by survival of the fittest. It is self-evident that species do vary and humans have selectively bred animals and plants since farming began. The

evidence suggested that this selection went on in the wild also.

3. There seemed to be many features that were common to a huge variety of species, eg the pentadactyl 'hand' or 'foot'. This suggested a common ancestry.

4. There seemed to be certain organs or features which, though useful in some species, seemed to be of little or no use in others. These were called vestigial organs. This suggested that these organs had been sidelined in a species as no longer of use, but also suggesting the species has a common ancestry with species that did use these organs.

5. Apparent 'imperfect design'. He observed that some organs or features looked like mere adaptations of earlier organs used for different purposes. This, he argued, suggested undirected adaptation, or to use a bit of slang, some organisms looked cobbled together rather than purpose-built.

From this evidence and deductions from the evidence, Darwin drew up his theory.

He suggested that, given sufficient time, the variations *within* a species that we observe today could lead to the production of a completely *new* species. He proposed that therefore the earliest form of simple life could, over millions of years, change gradually into a more sophisticated animal or plant by mutation (a random change in a feature or features), then by *selection of the fittest*. The mutation gives a small advantage in survival and therefore that variation survives to breed and so pass on its advantage. By a long accumulation of such little steps the vast array of life on earth could come about.

Darwin did not know about genes. Mendel's work on sweet peas had not yet been published. Darwin assumed that the mechanism of possible variation in a species was continuous, eg the colour of a flower could vary infinitely across a spectrum.

Mendel's work showed that this was not the case, but that variation within a species acted in discrete packages.

Mendel pioneered work in the science of genetics. But the main lesson we learn even today is that variations are the result of discrete changes of a gene or a group of genes. These discrete changes are not very amenable to Darwin's original supposition of tiny gradual steps of change.

Darwin was aware of one or two major objections to his theory. One was the fossil record itself—data; the other was a problem of how a specific organ could have evolved, where a partly constructed organ would be of little use to the animal or plant (a wing or the eye being cases in point).

The Fossil Record

Although the principle of Succession of Species was clearly shown in the fossil record, there was little support for the idea that the change toward more sophisticated species was gradual. The fossil record strongly suggested the opposite: sudden bursts of new species—sudden, that is, in geological time. Darwin suggested that this picture was an illusion: it was simply that the fossil record was then too fragmentary to show the gradual changes his theory predicted. At the time this suggestion was allowable. Indeed, it was a prediction that would help to support the theory, if the prediction proved correct.

Prediction: that as the gaps in the fossil record were filled in the gradual changes called for by Evolution would emerge.

Problem: this cannot be proven. The much more complete fossil record known today still features 'sudden' jumps, not gradual changes.

It would seem likely that Darwin made an elementary error in confusing observed *variation* with hypothetical *evolution*. He was using the method called extrapolation. The question is whether it was an appropriate method to use on the evidence available.

To illustrate the method take the example of human population growth: figures are available for world population growth going back, let us say, 100 years. From these figures statisticians will extrapolate into the future, ten years ahead, then say fifty years ahead, then a hundred years ahead. Each extension of time will inevitably reduce the reliability of the extrapolation: the further away you move from the time of the data the less useful the result and statisticians know this and warn accordingly. Inappropriate extrapolation can lead to some very silly results. Sadly, such inappropriate extrapolations are very common in Recent Creationist books: the speed of light extrapolation and the variations in the earth's magnetic field extrapolations are 'good' examples of bad extrapolation.

But Darwin made a similar error. He extrapolated the possibility of *evolution* from one species to another from the tiny *variations* observed within a species group. Over a few years it can sometimes be possible to actually observe minor variations occurring (the peppered moth is an often quoted example), but for a mere few decades' worth of data to then extrapolate backwards through hundreds of millions of years, just on the basis of the observed data, is inappropriate.

Thought experiment

His second problem, exemplified by the eye, he dealt with in a rather imaginative manner: the thought experiment. The same argument is used today by the likes of Dawkins and others to counter the design argument.

Regarding the eye, Darwin suggested that we can imagine a series of little steps from a very simple light-sensitive group of cells that just responded to night and day—which might give a simple creature an advantage in feeding—then becoming a patch which could detect direction of light (the cells being at the bottom of an indentation of some kind) and perhaps movement, all the way up to the human eye in a series of little advances of function. To put it another way, Darwin proposed that any apparent difficulty could be solved by a *Just So Story*, such as Rudyard Kipling later delightfully wrote for his children. Only Kipling's stories were just that: stories to divert children (and I think adults also), full of imagination and humour. Darwin's stories are just dull but equally untrue. Telling aetiological stories is as old as humanity.

Because, of course, one can indeed *imagine* such a sequence of little steps and one cannot absolutely disprove that this could not have happened. It is true that some of these proposed intermediate 'eyes' do exist in nature. But it is also true that from very early times highly sophisticated eyes also existed in very 'primitive' creatures of similar age: the Trilobite, for example, had an amazing eye, fully equipped and very efficient.

Darwin had fallen into the trap of Cartesian rather than Newtonian scientific method. If you remember, Descartes used 'imagination and mathematical modelling'—and here is Darwin doing the same but without the use of mathematical modelling.

But so confident was Darwin that his theory was correct that he stated:

> "If it could be possibly shown that any complex organ existed, which could not possibly have been formed by numerous, successive, slight modifications, my theory would absolutely break down. But I can find no such case." [*Origin,* p.182]

To which one might comment, "So that's alright then!" At first sight this looks as if Darwin has given us a prediction from his theory which could be a proper test for falsification. But it is an illusion. Since we can use a thought experiment alone to explain the origin of a complex organ, the ingenuity of human imagination will always suffice to take us over the hurdle!

Vestigial Organs

One of the strange things about the list of these organs is that it has rapidly been diminishing. The Victorian list was based on sheer ignorance of function. As no use could be seen for the tonsils they were called vestigial: often children's tonsils were removed at the slightest hint of tonsillitis. Only in more recent times was it discovered that the organ has a specific function in children in the development of the jaw and controlling infections. Subsequent discoveries have found that nearly all such vestigial organs have functions within the body.

Argument for evolution from 'imperfect design'

This is perhaps the great Achilles' heel in the argument for evolution used by Darwin and his successors to the present day.

Simply put, it is that some organs or even whole organisms look badly or imperfectly designed for their purpose.

90

If we take the human eye again, for example. Though a remarkable piece of kit, there appears to be a strange design flaw. The light-sensitive cells of the retina which register the light signals and transfer them by nerve impulses to the brain are *behind* the very nerve axons ('wiring') which take the signal to the visual cortex in the brain. These axons trail across the surface of the retina and then exit as a bundle through a hole in the back of the eye which is called the blind spot. Surely, it is argued, any *designer* would have put the light-sensitive cells in front of the nerve axons, thus removing two problems at a stroke: the loss of clarity caused by light having to pass through the nerve axons before reaching the retina and also removing the need for the blind spot.

At first sight this looks a rather strong argument in favour of 'blind' evolution.

But there are several serious problems with this. Behind this argument lies a curious piece of metaphysics.

The evolutionist is making use of some odd theological ideas about God. What they are in essence saying (as indeed several text books on evolution do say) is that they think they know how the Creator (if he existed) would have created life in all its varieties— usually they are assuming a very specific and narrow view—that he would make each creature individually, perfectly designed for its niche in creation. They often have in mind these days the Young Earth ideas about this.

Because they find that creatures do not appear to be 'perfectly' designed, it follows that their version of 'God' could not have created them; therefore evolution must be true as the only naturalistic explanation.

This type of argument is almost universal in books about Evolution, but:

1. We do not yet fully understand how every aspect of the human eye works, therefore it is premature to declare that we could envisage a better design.

2. How, anyway, can we presume to know how the Creator would create?

Once again there is a long history behind such presumptions. By the Victorian Age academic theology had become very 'liberal'. God was a smiling Providence: clergy spoke much about the fittingness of everything in creation: everything in its place and a place for everything. Such ideas are not really biblical at all, but go back to Greek philosophy and the Greek concept of perfection: the perfect human body, the perfect building design, the perfection of mathematics etc. after the ideas of philosophers like Plato. So God becomes an embodiment of this Greek concept of 'perfection'. This is what happens when you start, not from Biblical revelation, but from abstract philosophical ideas about the nature of God.

Such 'fittingness' is well characterised even in some Victorian hymns such as *All Things Bright and Beautiful* (remembering the verse often omitted in modern hymn books about "the rich man in his castle, the poor man at his gate...").

Many scientists before Darwin used this fittingness as a paradigm for the study of the living world. For Darwin, however, this paradigm did not fit his observations—he thought he could see that nature was not 'the best of all possible worlds'. It was 'red in tooth and claw' (as Tennyson was to write). There appeared to be huge waste and apparent cruelty. This did not look at all like the product of this smiling benevolent Providence of Victorian theology. Strangely some of his ideas about evolution were an attempt to detach this 'God' from his creation. A good God could not be directly responsible for such a cruel and wasteful nature. In fact, Darwin may well have believed in God in a very distant sense, but the God he believed in was not really responsible for creating this world of waste and carnage. Evolution was in part an attempt to separate God from natural 'evil', in the same way as Milton had attempted to separate God from moral evil in *Paradise Lost*. It is perhaps no coincidence that Darwin's constant companion on his voyage with *The Beagle* was Milton's *Paradise Lost*.

If we understand this mindset of Darwin we can see why he so often uses the reactive argument: 'God would not have done it this way, so therefore it must be Evolution.' In truth, the real power of Evolution as an idea lies with this reactive theology. Take that away from the

92

theory and the rest of the evidence is either a series of truisms or very ambivalent.

One might summarise it by saying that Evolution is simply a piece of negative theology surrounded by truisms. The truisms are that species vary and adapt to their environment by the natural selection of a favourable variation through the survival of the fittest. There is nothing particularly startling about these things—we can see this happening all around us if we are observant.

Connecting with this is the fact that Evolution is an extraordinarily flexible theory. It can accommodate pretty well anything. This makes it a very bad theory and certainly pretty useless scientifically: a theory that accommodates anything can make no meaningful predictions. The predictions that it does make are so general as to be, again, scientifically of no value.

With the exception of the fossil record—where it really does stub its toe—no worthwhile predictions have ever been made. Instead, it merely adapts to the evidence. Thus, even regarding the fossil evidence, instead of a steady gradual succession, neo-Darwinism and its successors now talk about 'punctuated equilibria'—long periods of stasis followed by rapid change where evolution is supposed to be working overtime! This is all very well, but this is no longer Darwin's theory, it is something else, but still does not tell us how this process takes place and, what is more, removes some of the necessity, essential for Darwinism to operate, for long periods of time.

As an example of how adaptable Evolution can be is its accommodation to the discovery of the Genetic Code. Before the structure and subsequently the code of DNA was worked out, Evolution had no meaningful prediction about what sort of code it might be: would it be universal or would each 'evolved' species have adapted its own code? Evolution could easily accommodate either possibility. But when Francis Crick demonstrated that it was a universal code it was hailed as a proof of Evolution. But of course it is no such thing. A theory that vaguely predicts either A or B cannot then say that because B is found to be the case it proves the theory. Particularly as A and B were the only possible alternatives: you might as well have spun a coin!

Continental Objectors to Darwinism

Alan Hayward, in his book, *Creation and Evolution,* collected an interesting group of continental biologists, zoologists and botanists who disagree with Darwinism and neo-Darwinism. I quote the following sections at length:

Because English is fast becoming the international language of science, English-speaking scientists have little incentive to learn foreign languages. Unfortunately, this makes it easy for them to become inward-looking. They tend to forget that a great deal of valuable scientific work is still being published in foreign languages.

This probably explains how most British and American biologists acquired the curious – and incorrect – notion that 'practically everybody accepts Darwinism'. If they had paid a little more attention to what was going on in continental Europe they would have known better.

For instance, they would not have been so bewildered when a book by the Scandinavian biologist, Erik Nordenskiöld, appeared in English translation in 1929 [*The History of Biology: a Survey,* transl. L. B. Eyre, Kegan Paul London 1929]. This stated that Darwin's theory of the origin of species 'was long ago abandoned. Other facts established by Darwin are all of second-rate value.'...

One of the greatest histories of science ever produced is a series of volumes written by various French scientists in the nineteen-sixties. This later appeared in English translation as *A General History of the Sciences.* In volume 4 the section on evolution is written by one of France's most eminent biologists, Professor Andrée Tétry.

She discusses what she calls 'the two great theories of evolution', Lamarckianism and Darwinism, as well as some lesser theories, and dismisses them all as inadequate. Her conclusion is:

In point of fact none of the theories we have been discussing provides an entirely satisfactory account of all the facts of evolution.

She is particularly hard on neo-Darwinism, which is sometimes called the 'synthetic theory' of evolution. Her description of it as 'the theory... which is favoured by British and American geneticists' is a clear hint that the rest of the world is a lot more sceptical of Darwinism than the Anglo-Saxons are.

She says it is 'hard to believe' that complex organs – and above all the human brain – could really have been produced by mutations, which are controlled by sheer chance. To do any good, she points out, a mutation must not only happen to be an exceedingly fortunate step forward – it must also 'adjust itself to the preceding mutation, and occur at precisely the right place and time.' In other words, for anything to evolve through a series of useful mutations, there would have to be a quite incredible succession of lucky chances. After listing her objections she sums up:

> No wonder, therefore, that J. Kälin has called the synthetic theory [neo-Darwinism] a kind of 'synthetic euphoria'.

...She ranks as one of France's leading evolutionists. But like many French biologists, she would rather say, 'We don't yet know how things could have evolved', than pretend that a bad theory is a good one.

And her words were written in the middle nineteen-sixties, when evolutionists all over the English-speaking world were loudly proclaiming, 'No respectable biologists doubt the truth of Darwinism.' It is no wonder that continentals sometimes accuse the British and Americans of arrogance and isolationism!

A French Botanist

In 1967 Dr Pierre Gavaudan, holder of the Chair in Botany and Cytology at the University of Poitiers, published a paper on evolution in the proceedings of a conference at an American university. Its purpose was to inform the Anglo-Saxon biologists why he thought they were foolish to swallow Darwin's theory so uncritically. He called neo-Darwinism an 'ingenious romance', and compared it to an eighteenth-century French writer who was said to have 'exalted nonsense to the level of genius'. More plainly, he declared:

> The pretence of neo-Darwinism to be able to open on its own account the door to truth looks a little childish.

In support of this conclusion he gave various reasons drawn from his researches in botany. One of the most impressive was based on carnivorous plants, which trap insects and digest them. This ability to obtain airborne nourishment gives them a tremendous advantage, since they can flourish in very poor soils where other plants have a job to survive. So one might have expected large parts of the world to be overrun with carnivorous plants, quietly digesting their mosquito steaks. Yet in fact they are quite rare.

How did this extraordinary behaviour arise? The digestive systems of these plants are highly complex, and there seems no way they could have evolved in a multitude of small steps. And, if they really are a triumphant success of natural selection – 'the survival of the fittest' – why are there so few carnivorous plants around? He answers:

> The [Darwinian] theory is incapable of giving anything better than a highly fictional description of the origin of these remarkable arrangements.

...He does not accept creation as the obvious alternative. Instead, he argues that there must be some mysterious property of living things that compels them to evolve along pre-determined lines. But is that an explanation...?

A French Zoologist

Pierre-Paul Grassé is no ordinary evolutionist. Some years ago he was described by a famous American Darwinist as:

> The most distinguished of French zoologists, the editor of the 28 volumes of *Traité de Zoologie*, author of numerous original investigations and ex-president of the Académie des Sciences. His knowledge of the living world is encyclopedic...

In his post as Director of the Laboratory of the Evolution of Living Beings, which is part of the University of Paris, he has been responsible for a great deal of research into the mechanism of evolution. Few men in all the world are better qualified to express an opinion about evolution.

In 1973 he published in French a major book on evolution, which appeared in English translation in 1977 [*Evolution of Living Organisms*]. Its purpose was twofold. First and foremost, the book aims to expose Darwinism as a theory that does not work, because it clashes with so many experimental findings. As he says in his introduction:

> Today our duty is to destroy the myth of evolution... some people, owing to their sectarianism, purposely overlook reality and refuse to acknowledge the inadequacies and the falsity of their beliefs. (p.8)

Then follow 200 large pages packed with evidence that Darwinism is on an entirely wrong track. Only after that does he turn to his second purpose, which is to offer a new theory of evolution to replace Darwin's.

His attack on Darwinism has many prongs, but its main thrust is aimed at the central idea of Darwinism: that evolution is due to the combined effect of (1) mutations, and (2) natural selection.

Mutations are the result of 'copying errors' in the genes. When a plant or animal reproduces, the new generation is usually almost exactly like the parents. The genes are extremely complex chemical substances in the germ cells, and they contain a sort of blueprint of the parents which is passed on to the next generation. If something goes slightly wrong when the genes duplicate themselves, the result may be a four-leafed clover, or the first copper beech tree, or a baby with twelve toes.

Such mutations give natural selection something to work on. Occasionally a mutant offspring is better equipped for survival than its normal brothers and sisters. When that happens the normal variety may die out locally, while the unusual one takes its place. And if that happens often enough, said Darwin, the outcome may be a new species. To summarize:

Mutation + natural selection = Darwinian evolution.

The only trouble is, says Grassé, that neither mutation nor natural selection works the way that Darwinists think they do!

Take mutation first. Grassé has studied this extensively, both inside his laboratory and in nature. In all sorts of living things, from bacteria to plants and animals, he has observed that mutations do not take succeeding generations further and further from their starting point.

Instead, the changes are like the flight of a butterfly in a greenhouse, which travels for miles without moving more than a few feet from its starting point. There are invisible but firmly fixed boundaries that mutations can never cross. As Grassé says:

> This text [a Darwinist book] suggests that modern bacteria are evolving very quickly, thanks to their innumerable mutations. *Now, this is not true.* For millions, or even billions, of years, bacteria have not transgressed the structural frame within which they have always fluctuated and still do... *To vary and to evolve are two different things*; this can never be sufficiently emphasized. (p.6 – his italics.)

> Despite their innumerable mutations, *Erophila verna* [whitlow grass], *Viola tricola* [wild pansy], and the rest do not evolve. *This is a fact.* (p.225 – his italics.)

He insists that mutations are only trivial changes; they are merely the result of slightly altered genes, whereas 'creative evolution... demands the genesis of new ones' (p.217). Other biologists agree with this, he claims, and quotes an American geneticist who has argued that 'big leaps in evolution required the creation of new gene loci with previously non-existent functions' (p.218). But he offers no real explanation of how nature can 'create' new genes.

98

Turning to natural selection, he shows that this frequently does not work in a Darwinian fashion, either. For example, he asks why should goats and deer have developed scent glands that enable them to keep track of each other (a minor advantage) but which give them away to the carnivores that hunt them (a major disadvantage)? After a detailed examination of the way natural selection works, he concludes:

Selection tends to eliminate the causes of a population's heterogeneity and thus to produce a uniform genotype. *It acts more to conserve the inheritance of the species than to transform it.* (p.119—his italics.)

Although Grassé is a convinced evolutionist, he enthuses over the wonders of nature as heartily as any creationist. In particular, he mentions many organs and mechanisms in nature that will work only when they are complete. For Darwinism to suggest that mutation and natural selection could produce such things is sheer romancing, he insists.

One of his examples is the mechanism that causes blood to clot when it is exposed to air. This is essential to animal life: without it, a small scratch and we should bleed to death.

Yet the system only works because a whole collection of different, and highly complex, chemical substances act *together* to achieve the desired result. Remove just one of those vital chemicals, and the blood won't clot any more. How could natural selection create such a system, asks Grassé. Only if its action were 'prophetic', he answers! In other words, it couldn't.

Another of his many examples is the ant-lion larva. This remarkable insect lives in regions of dry sand or sandy soil, where it digs a pit about two inches deep and waits at the bottom for ants to tumble in. It has a delicate intruder-alarm system, sensitive to the slightest vibration. If a single grain of sand rolls into the pit the ant-lion springs to the alert, with its pincer-like mandibles gaping, ready to seize its prey. The underside of its body is provided with a set of horn-like anchors, so that it can grip the soil while struggling with its captive.

The ant-lion's mouth is quite extraordinary, being fastened almost shut with a complicated locking system. This makes it unable to eat solid food, but the mouth forms a kind of drinking straw, ideally suited to supping broth.

Having grabbed an ant, the first thing the ant-lion does is to inject a paralysing drug. Then it gives a second injection of digestive juices which gradually turn the ant's insides into a nourishing liquid, ready for the ant-lion to suck it out.

There is no drinking water in the hot, dry sandpits where ant-lions live. Most insects would soon die of dehydration in such an environment. But not the ant-lion. To begin with, he is provided with an impermeable skin which, like the aluminium foil around a roasting chicken, prevents his body moisture from drying up. And his digestive tract has a system for recycling the urine, as astronauts do in a spaceship, so that every drop of water can be used again and again.

For such a creature to have evolved along Darwinian lines, Grassé comments, it would have needed 'an avalanche of coordinated and mutually adjusted chance occurrences' (p.163). The odds in favour of that, he declares, are 'infinitesimal' – a scientific way of saying that it is just not on.

Elsewhere he discusses the origin of the eye. He asserts that there is a better chance that dust blown by the wind might have produced Dürer's 'Melancholia' (a great sixteenth-century engraving) than that the eye was the result of copying errors in the gene (p.104).

For reasons like these Grassé – who, remember, has been acknowledged as one of Europe's greatest zoologists – rejects Darwinism as demonstrably false. He calls it a 'pseudoscience' (p.6) depending on frequent miracles (p.103), and says that Darwinists only look at those facts that fit their theory (p.50). They look upon chance as 'a sort of providence', which they do not name but 'secretly worship' (p.107). Well might he ask:

> When is Darwinian doctrine going to be subjected to a thorough, critical re-evaluation? (p.128)

Aware that he must sound at times like a creationist, Grassé makes it clear that he is not (p.166). He also insists that he does not believe in vitalism, the idea that there is a mystical property of life which accounts for everything in nature (p.216).

Creation and Evolution, pages 22-29

The Molecular Challenge to Evolution

When Darwin sailed with *The Beagle*, collected his specimens and examined them under his microscope, he had no more idea about how these organisms worked than an intelligent Medieval monk would understand how a modern computer works just by looking carefully under the lid. Therefore it is all the more strange that his grand theory of life, so full of glorious ignorance about its actual mechanisms, came to be established as the basis of much modern biology.

The truth is, the theory, being essentially a metaphysical theory, caught the mood of the Victorian academic world, already, like Darwin himself, disillusioned with the trite optimistic theology of the day. It was the rugged, macho, gritty alternative to the pious and sentimental teaching of much of the church at the time. Thus the theory was well bedded in before the serious objections, both philosophical and scientific, began to make their appearance. This has made it all the harder to displace.

In the decades following *Origin* it was seen as Biology's equivalent to Chemistry's Periodic Table of the Elements. The predictive power of Mendeleyev's *Periodic Table* had been a genuine triumph in Chemistry. Evolution was seen as Biology's way of getting in on the act of grand theories.

Let us return to our Medieval monk looking at a computer circuit board. He might observe that many of the bits looked like small black oblongs with various numbers of legs. He might correctly deduce that these objects were very important to the operation of the machine—if he removed even one of them, or just cut one leg, the machine would stop operating. But looking at them he might also conclude that they were simply black oblong objects and what they contained was simply more of the black material he could see on the outside.

As Darwin and his fellow biologists peered into their microscopes and could just see little blurred ovoid-shaped objects that seemed to make up much of the tissue of living creatures, they rightly concluded that these objects were very important for the operation of a living organism, but wrongly assumed that these objects were themselves very simple—mere blobs of jelly. The name *protoplasm* was given to their contents and they were thought not to be very complicated.

It is worth pointing out that another supposed piece of evidence for evolution was based on this inevitably superficial grasp of the real structures and functions of living things. Haeckel, a disciple of Darwin, produced his 'law', "Ontogeny recapitulates phylogeny". In plain English what this meant was that a developing embryo (ontogeny) of, say, a mammal goes through all the stages of the supposed evolutionary branch (phylogeny) it belongs to: from fish to reptile to mammal. From examination of the process it was thought that these different stages could be seen. Thus much was made of the fact that a human embryo at one stage looks as if it has gills (ie the fish stage!) etc. Little store is now placed on that idea as most of these 'likenesses' are just that: coincidental likenesses, but with little connection in function.

Just as our monk had no idea that within the little black oblongs was the most incredibly complex pattern of circuitry on a wafer of silicon, so Darwin and his successors had no idea that these 'cells' were themselves the most intricate pieces of sophisticated molecular machinery: each molecule an immensely complex structure, purpose built to carry out particular tasks to maintain the life of the cell.

But now we do know just how complex a 'simple' cell is. Since the 1950s there has been an explosion of understanding of the mechanisms within a single cell. And the chemistry of life is now understood pretty well at the very bottom of its 'well'. Darwin had no idea just how deep this well of complexity went, but now it can be said with reasonable certainty that biochemists have touched bottom. The mechanism of many of the vital chemical reactions of life are understood and the mechanism that maintains this chemistry is also well on the way to being understood. We are no longer like that Medieval monk peering at the black oblongs with legs; we now have excellent circuit diagrams of much that is etched onto the biochemical equivalent of those silicon wafers inside the oblongs.

And what has been discovered is not good news for Darwin's theory or even its modified versions. In fact, it is their worst nightmare. At the molecular level lies the same difficulty of how a complex structure like the eye could have evolved by blind processes of mutation and selection, but with this added difficulty. For the eye, Darwinism could get round the difficulties with the 'thought experiments'. If we could imagine a sequence of small changes from a simple light-sensitive spot to a complex eye, then Darwinism could say there was an explanation. But these thought experiments conveniently avoided having to look at actual detail. Precisely how even the small *imagined* changes were to have taken place was simply passed over—never mind the detail as long as the general outline made some kind of sense—the detail will become clear enough in the future when much more will be known about the molecular processes involved in sight.

Like politicians who make grand promises about taking some dramatic action in twenty years time—knowing that they won't have to be around to actually do anything about it, so too these early thought experiments simply put off the day when detailed explanations would be called for. But now that time has arrived with a vengeance.

Biochemists now know how the chemistry of sight works at the molecular level and, to use a hackneyed phrase, the devil really is in the detail! Even the simple light-sensitive spot is extremely complex in its chemistry: every enzyme and every chemical must come together at the same time. Such a scenario of producing even a light-sensitive part of a cell by chance really is impossible. Just for the process of light sensitivity the number of specifically 'designed' proteins and chemicals produced by these proteins runs into the hundreds. Yet all have to be there or the system doesn't work at all. In this case half a loaf is not better than none, it is worse! Half of a system in a cell that could make a light receptor would not survive in the cell for long as it achieves nothing except to use up valuable chemical energy which the cell needs for other functioning systems just to stay alive. At this level the 'thought experiment' becomes a hopeless exercise. Cartesian 'science' collapses in the face of hard chemical reality.

Darwinism is staring down the barrel of something called Irreducible Complexity and the gun is loaded.

A single cell is packed full of *irreducibly complex* machines, each machine essential for the life of the cell. If any machine goes wrong or isn't there, the cell is dead. There are delivery systems, more complicated than the Royal Mail, that deliver exactly the right chemical in exactly the right amount to exactly the right place at exactly the right time (I wish that for the Royal Mail!). Each 'parcel' has a specific address with a specific tag on it enabling the postal system to get it to exactly the right place in the cell. It is required to move across membranes, through 'hatches' into other machine areas, yet never to allow the wrong deliveries through as well. There are molecular machines that stitch together proteins (made up of multiples of the twenty different amino acids) hundreds or even thousands of amino acids long in exactly the right sequence, because if the sequence is wrong the protein is useless.*

Bovine Cytochrome c Oxidase, whose structure was elucidated by Dr Tsukihara in 1995.

* This picture gives just a hint of the extraordinary complexity of a single enzyme (a protein). Many hundreds of amino acids must be in exactly the right sequence or the molecule will not twist and fold into precisely the right shape to enable it to do its job.

It has information storage and duplication systems which have to function flawlessly at speeds way beyond anything a computer can do with the fastest hard drive and manipulating data files that are in the order of terabytes in size. All this at the molecular level. Many of these processes have been carefully studied and unravelled in recent decades.

None of them can work at all unless all the components are present and correct.

The *Flagellum* is a masterpiece of accurate and efficient engineering: it is a whip-like propeller used by 'simple' (!) single-celled bacteria as a means of propulsion. The idea that such a mechanism could come about by accident is quite absurd—and even though there are thousands of scientific papers on *Flagella*, not one suggests a remotely possible evolutionary pathway (in fact, there are just two papers in the world which make a stab at it—and fail).

> If you can, look on the Web at:
> www.nanonet.go.jp/english/mailmag/2004/011a.html
> scroll down to the video, *A Rotary NanoMachine,* and play it.

Darwinism really is helpless in the face of this barrage of reality. Look in the index for 'evolution' in any modern university-level text book on biochemistry and you will discover that there are very few references—where they exist they tend to be in the book's introduction where generalities are being talked about, almost never in the detailed biochemistry of the text. This is because Evolution has nothing to say about this; it cannot even start to come up with a meaningful explanation. The old generalities, that may have served earlier generations, simply won't wash any more. A full account of the idea of Irreducible Complexity is found in Michael Behe's *Darwin's Black Box* and further expanded in his *The Edge of Evolution.*

But it gets worse. Darwin called his book *On the Origin of Species,* but in fact it contained nothing of the sort! It did not explain at all how life began, just an attempt to explain how one animal or plant might become another animal or plant. Today 'origin of life research' is at a dead end. The initial high hopes of the early experiments have led nowhere. Many of those involved have moved to other more fruitful areas of research. If life has to begin by chance, then somehow a fully functioning cell must come together, capable of survival in a biochemically hostile environment and capable of reproduction. To reproduce means it must be able to pass on information of how to construct both the necessary machinery and information about the 'what, how and when' that machinery is to do its work. Information cannot appear by chance. The DNA molecule, where the data for every living cell is stored, cannot of itself come together in a random assembly to make information.

When Francis Crick cracked the code of DNA he also realised that there was a problem for the whole idea of blind forces.

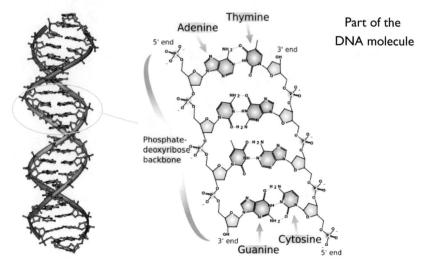

The molecule of DNA is like a ladder twisted into a helix: the vertical supports are made of a sugar (Deoxyribose) and phosphate, the rungs consist of two organic bases joined the middle. There are four of these bases, which are called: Adenine, Thymine, Guanine and Cytosine. We will abbreviate these to A,T,G,C. Chemically, A pairs only with T across the ladder and C pairs only with G across the ladder, but there is absolutely no preference as to which base is next to which along the same side of the ladder; in other words, the four bases can be in any order along one side of the ladder, but of course the other side must match up A to T, T to A, G to C, C to G. Herein is the unique design of the DNA molecule: when the cell divides it first needs to make a complete copy of the DNA. It does this by 'unzipping' the ladder and constructing two ladders out of the two half-ladders, but because of the A to T, C to G rule each new ladder is an exact replica of the original—simple but brilliant!

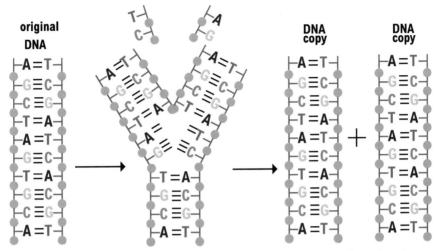

The four bases can form any sequence side by side. The 'letters', or *codons,* of the code are made up of three bases each, giving a total of 64 letters available. One or more letters code for one of the twenty amino acids used in protein building plus a stop code. Proteins perform nearly all the activities in the cell: motors, structural supports, chemical catalysis etc.*

* The DNA code:		Amino acid	DNA CODONS
Amino acid	**DNA CODONS**	Serine	TCT TCC TCA TCG AGT AGC
Isoleucine	ATT ATC ATA	Tyrosine	TAT TAC
Leucine	CTT CTC CTA CTG TTA TTG	Tryptophan	TGG
Valine	GTT GTC GTA GTG	Glutamine	CAA CAG
Phenylalanine	TTT TTC	Asparagine	AAT AAC
Methionine	ATG	Histidine	CAT CAC
Cysteine	TGT TGC	Glutamic acid	GAA GAG
Alanine	GCT GCC GCA GCG	Aspartic acid	GAT GAC
Glycine	GGT GGC GGA GGG	Lysine	AAA AAG
Proline	CCT CCC CCA CCG	Arginine	CGT CGC CGA CGG AGA AGG
Threonine	ACT ACC ACA ACG	'stop codons'	TAA TAG TGA

But what is the problem? Chemically there is no way useful information along the ladder in base sequences can be created by chance. All you would get if you had a random soup of bases is 'noise'. Crick was all too aware of this and, though he is an atheist, decided therefore that as DNA data could not have arisen by chance on earth it must have been planted by 'aliens'. If an atheist, faced with the DNA molecule, has to go to such lengths to avoid a reasonable conclusion of Design, then there is a serious problem for the blind chance explanation of the origin of life. In fact, Crick's idea merely pushes the origin problem out into the Universe. Where did this 'alien' DNA come from?

Let us summarise the evidence against evolution.

1. It is at heart a metaphysical explanation: 'God would not have done things like this, therefore evolution must be the explanation.' This presumes we know how God would do things, which the Bible is careful to avoid telling us!

2. Without severe modification Evolution cannot account for the fossil record which continues to strongly suggest dramatic leaps forward, not the slow gradualistic process predicted by Darwin.

3. The superficially plausible 'thought experiments', used to account for structures like the eye, fall apart when pressed to explain *exactly* how these imagined processes took place.

4. At the molecular level Darwinian explanations simply fall silent. But this is just where they must work best if the theory is to stand up to modern biochemistry.

But the riposte can often be, "Can you think of a better explanation?" To which the answer is, yes—Design.

Philosophy professor Antony Flew, after a lifetime of academic atheism, recently declared that he could not accept that the DNA molecule's information was created by natural processes and accepted that there must be an Intelligence behind the Universe. He commented, "We must follow the evidence wherever it leads."

But we need to deal with some real objections, some of which have already arisen.

The Watchmaker—Blind or Intelligent?

In 1802 Revd William Paley (1743-1805), an abolitionist clergyman and scholar, put forward his watchmaker analogy for his argument for Design. To paraphrase his argument in brief:

Imagine walking on a moor and coming across a stone lying on the path. How did it get there? Was it there for a purpose? No. But now suppose you come across a watch lying on the heath. Was it made by accident, like the stones and rocks around it, or was it made for a purpose and by an intelligent designer? Unlike the stone it has mechanisms, in this case clockwork, and shows a purpose—to tell the time. Just so we see design all around us in the mechanisms of nature and therefore deduce a Designer.

This argument from design for the existence of the Creator is much ridiculed today by the proponents of 'blind' evolution. So much so that Prof. Richard Dawkins published a book entitled *The Blind Watchmaker* in part parody of Paley's idea and to put forward his atheistic views.

However, when an idea is merely ridiculed one might rightly be suspicious that proper refutation may be lacking.

Although aspects of Paley's argument can be properly refuted, the reality is that his central premise has never been refuted. It is, in essence, similar to that of Irreducible Complexity.

Dawkins fails to deal with this issue. He picks off some of Paley's peripheral arguments successfully (and, to be fair to Dawkins, with an element of patronising respect towards someone he sees as a defeated but honourable enemy), but he does not address the core issue.

Paley himself perhaps did not quite see the force of his own basic premise and in his exposition of his analogy often took off into arguments about beauty and fittingness and tended to focus too much on the non-essential parts of his watch—the watch glass, the use of brass to prevent rust etc. These are not required by the basic purpose of the watch—they are not part of its irreducible complexity. So maybe we cannot wholly blame Dawkins for focusing on these weaknesses. nonetheless, Dawkins (and to my knowledge no-one else either) has ever refuted Paley's fundamental premise: that the watch is not only designed, but has a designer who knew what he wanted the watch to do.

Dawkins himself, when trying to deal with the biochemical impasse, falls into the trap of having to call on purpose and design.

He claims he can show how a functioning protein could come about quite easily by chance—but unfortunately he fails to see that his 'chance' is purpose driven. His way round the nigh impossible odds of blind forces making a successful protein is to assume that in a long string of 'letters' somehow, as different combinations accidentally occur, a 'letter' in the right place (by chance) will stay there for the next 'shake of the dice'.

Suppose you have five dice and you want to throw five sixes. In a 'blind watchmaker' biochemical soup all you have is all the dice being thrown each time.

But Dawkins argues that if you get one six in your throw of five dice, you can take that one out and then throw four dice and if you get a six, remove that one and throw three dice and so on until you get the five sixes.*

---

* The chances of throwing all five sixes in one throw are:
    $1/6 \times 1/6 \times 1/6 \times 1/6 \times 1/6$, ie 1 in 7776.
    In five throws, it is 1 in 1555.
    But by extracting each six as it occurs, in the first throw the chances of getting a six are now 5 in 6,
        in the second throw it becomes 4 in 6; in the third it become 3 in 6
        in the fourth 2 in 6; in the fifth 1 in 6
    The chances of getting the five sixes in just five throws are now reduced to a mere $5/6 \times 4/6 \times 3/6 \times 2/6 \times 1/6$, ie 1 in 65.
    The figures, however, for just one real protein of around 1000 animo acids long are mind-boggling:
    The blind chances are 1 in 10^{1300}, that is a 1 with 1300 noughts after it.
    There have been only about 4×10^{26} nanoseconds since Creation!

But this method requires an external 'intelligence' taking out the required sixes as they appear and knowing that a six is what is required. But Dawkins does not believe there is such an intelligence, so he has fudged his case. His 'blind' protein has no idea what sequence it wants to achieve. As Jesus said, "ye therefore do greatly err!"

If designed, why does it seem less than perfect?

The question that first needs to be put is, what do you mean by perfect? Once again, behind this issue of perfection lies, not the Biblical view of creation being *tov* = good, but the Greek understanding of perfect, of the sort derived from Plato's view of archetypes. This is a very icy and clinical view of 'perfect': perfectly proportioned etc. But strangely this view is not very pleasing to human eye or ear. A perfect face as sometimes portrayed in fashion magazines is often very dull. A real human face which attracts us is something far deeper than that—indeed, the face is seldom if ever equally proportioned, but its very attractiveness may lie more in its differences rather than anything else.

Or a musical instrument: one that is played by the human artist sounds so much better than the clinical, even though nouanced, performance of a synthetic musical instrument, even if produced by the best computer.

The tick of a real grandfather clock is better than the tick of a quartz-regulated mechanism.

A proper pipe organ is better than a digital organ.

This is a subtle matter to tease out, but Greek perfection is a flawed understanding.

The Biblical view is rather different. Genesis speaks of Creation being good—*tov* [translated *KALOS* in Greek in the *LXX*; meaning: sound, hale or whole], which means pleasing, satisfying, as opposed to *yapeh*, which means 'beautiful' in the Greek sense.

If we look at the *LXX* again, it uses *KALOS* for good in the sense of 'fit for purpose', rather than *AGATHOS,* which means 'morally good'. In other words, creation is good (or even very good) in that it behaves as God wants it to behave—it is 'fit for purpose'.

The trouble for us in the 21st century is that we see creation (nature) through distorting lenses.

First is the Greek philosophical lens: their sense of perfection and the fittingness of things is unreal. This persisted in European thought and played quite a part in the process of both pre-scientific and scientific discovery. Ancient astronomy saw the heavens as 'perfection' (outside fallen earth), where objects moved in perfect mathematical patterns—circles or epicycles. Even with the new astronomy of Copernicus, he still tried to maintain perfect circles. Kepler and Newton broke this Greek principle by discovering and mathematically modelling the elliptical orbits of the planets; even then Newton had some problems with orbital wobbles (due to the weak gravitational interaction with other planets), which he put down to God making occasional adjustments! It was Laplace who sorted this out and supposedly replied to Napoleon, who had asked him where God was in his theories, "I have no need of that hypothesis!"

Then comes the Victorian 'optimistic' lens, where, as science progressed and human material conditions began to improve, the element of sentimentality entered into the view of nature: the 'benevolent Providence' touched on earlier: "All things bright and beautiful". The suffering of animals began to be a matter of moral concern. This was of course to become even stronger as the 20th century took its course. As Robin Page wrote in his book, *The Hunting Gene*, "enter Bambi". This Victorian sentimentality becomes very distorted.

As we saw, it was this very 19th-century sentimentality that in part Darwin was revolting against, but at the same time it was the negative 'fuel' driving his Evolutionary philosophy: the apparent conundrum: if God is all good and all powerful, why does he allow suffering and cruelty? To allow it either means he is not all good or is unable to stop it, therefore is not all powerful.

Yet the Bible does not start from such a position: as the angel answers Joshua's question before the battle of Jericho, "Are you for us or for our enemies?" "Neither," he replied (Josh. 5:14-15). First of all God is God, and he is indeed good, but he creates a world as he wills which may not always seem to us as 'perfect' in the Greek sense.

5 "I am the LORD, and there is no other;
Besides Me there is no God.
I will gird you, though you have not known Me;
6 That men may know from the rising to the setting of the sun
That there is no one besides Me.
I am the LORD, and there is no other,
7 The One forming light and creating darkness,
Causing well-being and creating calamity;
I am the LORD who does all these."

Is 45:5-7 NASB

Victorian sentimentality tended to overlook these kinds of texts, wanting to focus too much on the benevolence of God.

13 The wings of the ostrich flap joyfully,
but they cannot compare with the pinions and
feathers of the stork.
14 She lays her eggs on the ground
and lets them warm in the sand,
15 unmindful that a foot may crush them,
that some wild animal may trample them.
16 She treats her young harshly, as if they were not hers;
she cares not that her labour was in vain,
17 for God did not endow her with wisdom
or give her a share of good sense.
18 Yet when she spreads her feathers to run,
she laughs at horse and rider.

Job 39:13-18

God reveals he has not made things that necessarily fit into *our* scheme of how things should be.

19 The creation waits in eager expectation for the sons of God to be revealed.
20 For the creation was subjected to frustration, not by its own choice, but by the will of the one who subjected it, in hope
21 that the creation itself will be liberated from its bondage to decay and brought into the glorious freedom of the children of God.
22 We know that the whole creation has been groaning as in the pains of childbirth right up to the present time.

Rom 8:19-22

Remember, God has prepared a New Heaven and a New Earth which will be eternal. Even before the Fall, this earth was never intended to be immortal in its original state.

9 Woe to him who quarrels with his Maker, to him who is but a potsherd among the potsherds on the ground.
Does the clay say to the potter, 'What are you making?'
Does your work say, 'He has no hands'?

Is 45:9

4 But the pot he was shaping from the clay was marred in his hands; so the potter formed it into another pot, shaping it as seemed best to him.

5 Then the word of the LORD came to me:

6 "O house of Israel, can I not do with you as this potter does?" declares the LORD. "Like clay in the hand of the potter, so are you in my hand, O house of Israel."

Jer 18:4-6

20 But who are you, O man, to talk back to God? "Shall what is formed say to him who formed it, 'Why did you make me like this?'"

21 Does not the potter have the right to make out of the same lump of clay some pottery for noble purposes and some for common use?

22 What if God, choosing to show his wrath and make his power known, bore with great patience the objects of his wrath—prepared for destruction?

Rom 9:20-22

These texts have a clear application to Israel, but behind them lies the principle that God may do as he chooses with his creation. He may choose to make animals who in due time become extinct: they serve a purpose in God's great scheme of things, very possibly hidden from us, but the potter making a pot and then remaking it reminds us of the impermanence of this world. As it says in Deut 29:29:

"The secret things belong to the LORD our God, but the things revealed belong to us and to our sons forever, that we may observe all the words of this law."

Nature is not our 'Mother', but rather a fellow 'creature' which has its own purposes, designed and created by God, which are not all purely designed for our benefit. It is perhaps unruly and God's original commission to human beings was, from the first, to tame and control it and to exploit its material riches.

28 God blessed them and said to them, "Be fruitful and increase in number; fill the earth and subdue it. Rule over the fish of the sea and the birds of the air and over every living creature that moves on the ground."

Gen 1:28

114

8 Now the LORD God had planted a garden in the east, in Eden; and there he put the man he had formed.

9 And the LORD God made all kinds of trees grow out of the ground—trees that were pleasing to the eye and good for food. In the middle of the garden were the tree of life and the tree of the knowledge of good and evil.

10 A river watering the garden flowed from Eden; from there it was separated into four headwaters.

11 The name of the first is the Pishon; it winds through the entire land of Havilah, where there is gold.

12 (The gold of that land is good; aromatic resin and onyx are also there.)

13 The name of the second river is the Gihon; it winds through the entire land of Cush.

14 The name of the third river is the Tigris; it runs along the east side of Asshur. And the fourth river is the Euphrates.

15 The LORD God took the man and put him in the Garden of Eden to work it and take care of it.

Gen 2:8-15

Why is there so much waste and carnage?

The fact that nature is apparently wasteful is a subjective value judgment on our part, as it was on Darwin's—who made this charge against God. I suppose we have tidy minds and waste seems untidy. Yet a moment's reflection on human creativity shows that discarding material (waste if you like) is part of creating, part of bringing order out of disorder. Once again, from Jeremiah 18:4,

But the pot he was shaping from the clay was marred in his hands; so the potter formed it into another pot, shaping it as seemed best to him.

"With so many past failures, you might think that environmental predictions would become more cautious. But not if it's a 'religion'. Remember, the nut on the sidewalk carrying the placard that predicts the end of the world doesn't quit when the world doesn't end on the day he expects. He just changes his placard, sets a new doomsday date, and goes back to walking the streets. One of the defining features of 'religion' is that your beliefs are not troubled by facts, because they have nothing to do with facts."

Michael Crichton (1942-2008)
'Remarks to the Commonwealth Club'
San Francisco, September 15, 2003

Part III
Climate Change

Chapter 10

Whom should we trust?

"For my thoughts are not your thoughts,
neither are your ways my ways,"
declares the LORD.
"As the heavens are higher than the earth,
so are my ways higher than your ways
and my thoughts than your thoughts.
As the rain and the snow
come down from heaven,
and do not return to it
without watering the earth
and making it bud and flourish,
so that it yields seed for the sower and bread for the eater,
so is my word that goes out from my mouth:
It will not return to me empty,
but will accomplish what I desire
and achieve the purpose for which I sent it."

Is 55:8-11

"Whan that Aprille with his shoures soote—
The droughte of March hath perced to the roote,
And bathed every veyne in swich licour
Of which vertu ungendred is the flour;"

The Canterbury Tales, Geoffrey Chaucer, 1386

"Our years are turned upside down; our summers are no summers; our harvests are no harvests!"

John King, *an Elizabethan preacher, 1595*

"It is strange what weather we have had all this winter; no cold at all but the ways are dusty and the flyes fly up and down and the rose bushes are full of leaves; such a time of the year as never was known in this world before."

Samuel Pepys' *Diary, 21st January 1661*

"Ordered by Parliament to pray for more seasonable weather; that it is, both as to warmth and every other thing, just as if it were the middle of May or June, which doth threaten a plague to follow."

Samuel Pepys' *Diary, 15th January 1662*

"Wind the last night (such as hath not been in memory before, unless at the death of the late protector*), that it was dangerous to go out of doors; and hearing how several persons have been killed today by the fall of things in the street and that the pageant in Fleet street is most of it blown down and hath broke down part of several houses."

Samuel Pepys' *Diary, 18th February 1662*

*Oliver Cromwell

"Is it not strange weather? Winter absorbed the Spring, and now Autumn is come before we have had summer: But let not our kindness for each other imitate the inconsistency of the seasons."

Dr Samuel Johnson, *11th September 1784*

If there is one truism it is that the weather is not very predictable. Climate can be loosely defined as 'weather averaged over a long period'. Thus we call the climate of Britain temperate, that of most of Africa tropical or equatorial, that of Siberia as Arctic etc. These are huge generalisations. The study of the patterns of these different kinds of climate give rise to further smaller generalisations, such that British weather is frontal, American weather tends to be airmass, Indian weather is characterised by monsoons, etc. Climate and its associated weather patterns are further affected by seasons, by the orbit of earth around the sun, which varies considerably over time (tens of thousands of years) and the precession of the earth's axis. All these things and many more factors—as we shall see—cause variations in the average climate in any part of the earth.

As the quotes above show, expected patterns of climate are frequently confounded by reality. Man has always tried to predict the weather as it can be a very important matter: as a farmer or a sailor it is very important to be as prepared as possible for the apparent vagaries of the weather.

[Jesus] *said to the crowd: "When you see a cloud rising in the west, immediately you say, 'It's going to rain,' and it does.*

55 And when the south wind blows, you say, 'It's going to be hot,' and it is.

56 Hypocrites! You know how to interpret the appearance of the earth and the sky. How is it that you don't know how to interpret this present time?

Lk 12:54-56

But nonetheless these short-term predictions were unreliable, as the storm on the lake recorded in the gospels makes clear.

A furious squall came up, and the waves broke over the boat, so that it was nearly swamped.

38 Jesus was in the stern, sleeping on a cushion. The disciples woke him and said to him, "Teacher, don't you care if we drown?"

39 He got up, rebuked the wind and said to the waves, "Quiet! Be still!" Then the wind died down and it was completely calm.

40 He said to his disciples, "Why are you so afraid? Do you still have no faith?"

41 They were terrified and asked each other, "Who is this? Even the wind and the waves obey him!"

Mk 4:37-41

Contained within this dramatic miracle is a vital truth: God is in charge of the weather and therefore, by extension, the Climate. When God gave Adam dominion over the earth he made no reference to the weather being in man's dominion.

God, if I might put it this way, reserves the control of weather for himself. Many references could be cited, including the one that heads this chapter from the Old Testament showing how the Jews grasped the fact that God decides the weather.

Many of the plagues and miracles of the Exodus were either directly or indirectly the result of the weather.

Then Moses left Pharaoh and went out of the city. He spread out his hands towards the LORD; the thunder and hail stopped, and the rain no longer poured down on the land.

Ex 9:33

The parting of the Red Sea was directly attributed to weather:

Then Moses stretched out his hand over the sea, and all that night the LORD drove the sea back with a strong east wind and turned it into dry land. The waters were divided, ...

Ex 14:21

God uses weather as a means of discipline:

Then the LORD's anger will burn against you, and he will shut the heavens so that it will not rain and the ground will yield no produce, and you will soon perish from the good land the LORD is giving you.

Deut 11:17

Now Elijah the Tishbite, from Tishbe in Gilead, said to Ahab, "As the LORD, the God of Israel, lives, whom I serve, there will be neither dew nor rain in the next few years except at my word."

1 Kings 17:1

After a long time, in the third year, the word of the LORD came to Elijah: "Go and present yourself to Ahab, and I will send rain on the land."

1 Kings 18:1

"I also withheld rain from you
when the harvest was still three months away.
I sent rain on one town,
but withheld it from another.
One field had rain;
another had none and dried up."

Amos 4:7

I form the light and create darkness,
I bring prosperity and create disaster;
I, the LORD, do all these things.
"You heavens above, rain down righteousness;
let the clouds shower it down.
Let the earth open wide,
let salvation spring up,
let righteousness grow with it;
I, the LORD, have created it."

Is 45:7-8

Do any of the worthless idols of the nations bring rain?
Do the skies themselves send down showers?
No, it is you, O LORD our God.
Therefore our hope is in you,
for you are the one who does all this.

Jer 14:22

Ask the LORD for rain in the springtime;
it is the LORD who makes the storm clouds.
He gives showers of rain to men,
and plants of the field to everyone.

Zech 10:1

Then the LORD sent a great wind on the sea, and such a violent
storm arose that the ship threatened to break up.

Jonah 1:4

Then the LORD answered Job out of the storm.

Job 38:1

After that, we who are still alive and are left will be caught up
together with them in the clouds to meet the Lord in the air. And so we
will be with the Lord for ever.

1 Thess 4:17

The Lord is in charge of the weather; no question. Today, in a humanist and atheistic world, such an idea is regarded as merely quaint and pre-scientific. Like the builders of Babel, humans now think *they* are causing the weather.* They believe that at any moment human activity may cause a tipping point toward a catastrophe.

* Some have compared this inverted *hubris* to the story of King Canute (Knut, 1014-1035). He was supposed to have tried to stop the tide coming in. In fact, the story is more interesting than that. Canute had started his reign as a pagan, but converted to Christianity. His court was full of pagan sycophants whom he wished to be rid of. When they tried to flatter him by saying he was so powerful that he could command the tide, he saw his opportunity. Down to the shore they went, but the tide came in as scheduled and Canute sacked the lot of them; a very astute man!

Behind these irrational fears lie perhaps two basic fallacies.

1. **Atheism:** if the world is a product of blind forces and life itself also resulted from 'chance and necessity', then random or careless actions by humans may kill off all life.
2. **'Fragile Earth':** this curious concept was probably brought into existence by a remark of Mike Collins, Apollo 11's Command Module astronaut. He recalls looking back at the earth and thinking that the earth looked so fragile. As a poetic and emotional feeling that is perfectly legitimate, but as a statement of reality, as it has been taken to be, it is nonsense. The earth is incredibly robust. It has 'survived' over four billion years of change, three atmospheres and encounters with asteroids and comets, going from iceball to hothouse and back. Life has thrived on it and shows no signs at all of weakening!

What of course these atheists ignore is that this planet (and Universe) is designed and sustained by our amazing God, who is also able to be every human being's heavenly Father if they repent and put their trust in the Living Word, the Lord Jesus Christ.

He came to that which was his own, but his own did not receive him. Yet to all who received him, to those who believed in his name, he gave the right to become children of God—children born not of natural descent, nor of human decision or a husband's will, but born of God.

Jn 1:11-13

Nevertheless, the world along with many Christians and Christian organisations are apparently convinced that human beings are changing the climate and that there will be apocalyptic consequences in just a few decades (according to a scary report produced by the WWF, *Climate Change: Faster, Stronger, Sooner,* the Arctic ice will be gone in five years). They all claim that there is a scientific 'consensus' and that 'the debate is over' and we must act now.

Before continuing, let me state that I too believe that a 'global warming' apocalypse is coming, but not in the way predicted by the current 'consensus'. What is coming is on a scale and magnitude beyond their comprehension and it will be God's doing, not human activity.

But do not forget this one thing, dear friends: With the Lord a day is like a thousand years, and a thousand years are like a day. The Lord is not slow in keeping his promise, as some understand slowness. He is patient with you, not wanting anyone to perish, but everyone to come to repentance.

But the day of the Lord will come like a thief. The heavens will disappear with a roar; the elements will be destroyed by fire, and the earth and everything in it will be laid bare. Since everything will be destroyed in this way, what kind of people ought you to be? You ought to live holy and godly lives as you look forward to the day of God and speed its coming.

That day will bring about the destruction of the heavens by fire, and the elements will melt in the heat. But in keeping with his promise we are looking forward to a new heaven and a new earth, the home of righteousness.

2 Pet 3:8-13

When dealing with a 'problem' such as Global Warming, it is vitally important to sort facts from theories, and even then to sort facts from fiction or hearsay. Too many of the discussions over Climate Change and its causes are conducted on the basis of hearsay by groups or organisations who ought to know better. Because of this many others who respect these organisations accept as fact what in reality is myth.

Whom do we trust?

We speak of accepting something on 'good authority'. But what is a good authority in this area? Let me go through a few well known organisations which are frequently cited by activists and politicians as 'good authorities'.

IPCC—the Intergovernmental Panel on Climate Change: The IPCC is often cited by politicians and activists as the leading global authority on Climate Change. Set up under the auspices of the United Nations, it had its impetus and origin from the UK in the work of the Hadley Centre (see below) in the early 1980s. It is itself made up of politicians, civil servants and leaders of NGOs and special interest environmental activist groups.

Its working group was co-chaired for many years by Sir John Houghton, an evangelical Christian environmental activist (some have called him an environmental fanatic). He has been influential in persuading many ill-informed Christian NGOs (eg Christian Aid and TearFund) to go with the greenhouse hypothesis. It has no scientists on its payroll, but gathers together scientific papers on the matter of climate change and its supposed global effects on food and water supply, spread of disease, population etc.

It holds conferences every five years or so and produces huge reports. Central to these reports are the *Summaries for Policy makers*. These summaries are supposed to do just that: summarise the conclusions derived from the myriad scientific papers produced by different groups tackling the different areas: from the climate itself, to its effects on disease, poverty, even 'sexism' etc. It all looks very thorough and impressive, but, as so often, a quick look under the bonnet shows that all is not what it appears to be.

The Hadley Centre (a department of the MetOffice). This organisation houses one of the few 'super computer climate modelling systems' in the world. It was set up in the early 1980s with a huge injection of government money. Margaret Thatcher had embraced the 'greenhouse hypothesis' as the moral basis for her fight with the coal miners. Coal-fired power stations 'increased global warming' by putting up CO_2 into the atmosphere. Mrs Thatcher wanted to go for nuclear generation as a secure option both against striking miners and the uncertainties of oil supplies from politically unstable parts of the world.

The Government's Chief Scientific Advisor: currently Prof. John Beddington appointed in October 2007. Formerly it was Prof. Sir David King. He it was who 'prophesied' that in a hundred years' time the only habitable continent would be Antarctica. They have often become mouthpieces for government propaganda.

NASA includes the Goddard Institute for Space Studies (GISS). Its chief, Dr James Hansen, is a climate change activist who has a tendency to use the, not very accurate, temperature figures to promote alarm. We need to be aware that many big bureaucracies, including many NGOs as well, are not averse to 'scaring up funding'. NASA has often struggled to get government funds. The Space Shuttle project was seriously hampered by lack of money. The original concept had to be greatly scaled back—with pretty catastrophic results in terms of astronauts' lives.

It is unfortunate that all these organisations, worthy and honourable though they may have been, have become spokespersons for the current hysteria. We will look in more detail later where some of these organisations have failed in their scientific duties and instead pursued activist or political agenda and why.

What are the facts about 'Greenhouse' gases?

It is beyond doubt that carbon dioxide (CO_2) levels have risen by more than 60% over the last century. This sounds very dramatic. But let me put matters in perspective. Here is a list of the gases in the atmosphere whose presence is stable. Water vapour is not included as amounts vary enormously from place to place and day to day. It also does not include very soluble gases such as sulphur dioxide which are rapidly removed from the atmosphere by rain and whose quantities also vary enormously depending on how industrialized a particular part of the globe is.

The amounts are expressed as % and then in parts per million (*ppm*) of dry air by volume:

gas	%	ppm
Nitrogen	78	780,900
Oxygen	21	209,500
Argon[1]	1	9,300
Carbon Dioxide[G]	0.038	380
Neon[1]	0.002	20
Helium[1]	0.0005	5
Methane[G]	0.0002	2
Krypton[1]	0.0001	1
Nitrous Oxide[G]	0.00005	0.5
Hydrogen	0.00005	0.5
Ozone[G]	0.00004	0.4
Xenon[1]	0.00001	0.1

1 = Inert gas (an element which has virtually no ability to form chemical compounds). G = 'Greenhouse' gas.

As can be seen from the table, the 'greenhouse' gases, carbon dioxide, methane and ozone make up only a very tiny amount of the atmosphere and the major 'greenhouse' gas is omitted from the table: water vapour.

What is the 'Greenhouse' effect?

Energy reaches the earth through the atmosphere from the sun. Much of it is high energy such as light. When the infrared energy reaches the earth's surface some is absorbed by the ground or ocean and is turned into heat. The ground or ocean warms and it too radiates energy—mostly in the low infrared (heat). It is argued that the 'greenhouse' gases let through most of the sun's energy, but absorb the lower energy infrared being radiated back into space, causing a

126

radiation trap within the atmosphere radiating heat back to the ground, which warms a bit more. That is what is argued. *But it is not correct.* Firstly, it is a fundamental law of physics that heat, by itself, cannot be transferred from a colder body to a hotter one: CO_2 and other infrared absorbing gases in the atmosphere are always cooler than the ground, so cannot warm the ground. Secondly, a real glass greenhouse is not a radiation trap: all that is happening is that the sun's radiation heats the ground inside a greenhouse which warms the air inside by conduction and convection. Since the air cannot escape it continues to be warmed by the ground and so the air temperature rises. The fact that the glass absorbs infrared is irrelevant. A greenhouse will warm even better if another transparent material is used which does *not* absorb infrared. Strangely this fact about greenhouses has been known since 1909, but never made it into the text books - primarily perhaps because, until the 1980s, no one thought it important. Thirdly, the atmosphere does not have the properties of a greenhouse anyway as there is no solid roof to trap the warming air. The greenhouse hypothesis of climate therefore is fundamentally wrong: it has been falsified by the experimental evidence. (see *Appendix 1 p223*)

CO_2 levels in the earth's atmosphere have varied enormously over millions of years, sometimes being ten or twenty times the current levels, and life on earth has not just survived, it has thrived on it. The last time they were as low as they are today was 300 million years ago.

Carbon dioxide is not a 'pollutant'

Without CO_2 there would be no life on earth. All vegetation depends on CO_2 for life and all animals ultimately depend on vegetation for life. Our bodies are made up mostly of water and products made from carbon dioxide.

Then God said, "I give you every seed-bearing plant on the face of the whole earth and every tree that has fruit with seed in it. They will be yours for food.

And to all the beasts of the earth and all the birds of the air and all the creatures that move on the ground—everything that has the breath of life in it—I give every green plant for food." And it was so.

Gen 1:29-30

Is the current rise in CO_2 level due primarily to human emissions? This is far from certain. The CO_2 cycle is very complex. When the oceans warm, CO_2 bubbles out like the gas in a soda water bottle. Warm water can hold (dissolve) less CO_2 than cold water—one reason why a chilled fizzy drink appears less frothy when opened than a warm one. Equally, dissolved CO_2 is taken in by sea plants and other creatures like algae, shellfish and molluscs. They convert CO_2 into shells and bones. On land, similarly, CO_2 is taken up by all plant vegetation to make the chemicals needed for life and growth. The more CO_2 in the atmosphere the quicker plants grow. Animals use vast amounts indirectly to form their bodies and much CO_2 is trapped in bones and in the shells and skeletons in the rivers and seas. Over millions of years huge amounts of CO_2 are converted into calcium carbonate ($CaCO_3$), which forms layers on the floors of the oceans. In due time, as the plates on the earth's surface move and underflow, the $CaCO_3$ is heated up in the volcanoes along the great tectonic plate lines on the earth's crust where CO_2 is once more spewed out in eruptions back into the atmosphere or back into the oceans to dissolve once again. We shall come back to the question about the current rise in CO_2 levels because some may well be due to processes that started a thousand years ago.

Recent Warming

It is accepted by pretty well everyone in the debate about climate change that there has been a modest rise in global average temperatures since 1880. It has not been a steady rise, as the graph opposite (flawed as it is) shows.

In passing it's worth noting that no scientist looking at the rise in CO_2 levels and the variation in global average temperature would see any obvious connection. The correlation is very poor and, remember, correlation is not causation. This graph, produced by the Goddard Institute for Space Studies (GISS), is a global average based to a considerable degree on the American continent from something like 1,500 ground-based weather stations of surface temperatures. America is used as a sample for the whole globe. This is reasonable as the weather station records go back pretty continuously over the last century and a

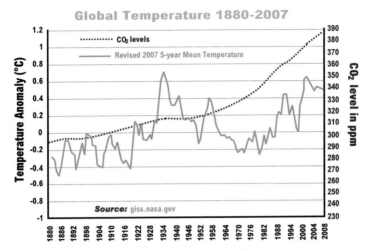

Global Temperature 1880-2007

Source: giss.nasa.gov

bit. Records from places like Russia and Europe are less consistent due to wars and revolutions, where daily records were lost or never even recorded for various periods.

But there are, nonetheless, very serious problems with this record.

1. It has been shown by two statisticians of repute (Steve McIntyre and Prof. Ross McKitrick) that the computer averaging program used by GISS is flawed—giving too much weight to recent rises.

2. A careful survey by Anthony Watts *(wattsupwiththat.com)*, a meteorologist, is showing up a very serious problem with the siting of the weather stations used for the survey. Clearly it makes sense to use where possible the same locations for the average temperature. But this presents a problem: weather stations which, a hundred years ago, were out in the country are now surrounded by urban or suburban development which is known to raise the local temperature by 2-3°C (that is ten to a hundred times greater than the change in temperature trying to be detected!). Around 40% of the sites currently surveyed (around 600 out of the 1500 as of going to press) are placed in wholly inappropriate places, such as near cooling fans from air conditioning plants or, in one instance of a station apparently well out in the hills of California, within five yards of a large swathe of tarmac—notorious for heating up the air several degrees above the true ambient temperature (see picture following).

A weather station in the Californian hills

3. Over the last three decades it has been possible to measure the overall temperature of the earth using geostationary satellites [that is, satellites that are orbiting in synchronisation with the rotating earth. This means they are always looking at the same part of the earth's surface]. These have consistently shown far less warming overall than the ground stations have done by around 40-50%.

However, there has been some very modest warming since 1880. In terms of overall climate trends this is hardly surprising and also generally to be welcomed, as we shall see.

To summarise so far: there has been a rise in atmospheric CO_2 and there has been a modest overall rise in average temperature, albeit erratic, in the last 130 years.

Chapter 11

Alarums, excursions and baseless fears

... But he who chases fantasies lacks judgment. Prov 12:11

Eight Wrongs do not make right

The advocates of man-made global warming are daily stoking up the hype by adding to these two basic facts a list of trouser-filling apocalyptic fears. Let us take them one at a time.

1. Global Warming will cause sea levels to rise dramatically—with the strong implication (as in Al Gore's film, *An Inconvenient Truth*) that coastal areas and low lying land will soon be inundated. **WRONG.**

The facts as measured by ocean scientists are otherwise. Since the middle of the last Ice Age around 18,000 years ago sea levels have, not unsurprisingly, risen considerably as the ice melts: the figure is about 400 feet (130m). If we calculate the rise in sea level per century, this means that sea levels would rise *on average* a little over two feet per century (just about 27 inches). We know that over the last three centuries, based on reasonably reliable tide gauges, the rate has remained fairly steady at about six inches per century. This means that initially the rise must have been much greater, but this again is what we would expect as there was an enormous amount of land based ice to melt. There is some evidence that the rate of sea level rise is slowing slightly, which again would be expected, though measuring small changes in sea level can be often as problematic as measuring global temperature.

The constant headlines about melting glaciers and the disappearance of the Arctic sea ice are unfortunately just bad journalism. Nothing remarkable is happening in the Arctic, as Professor Syun-Ichi Akasofu, Director of the International Arctic Research Centre, stated (in an interview in *The Great Global Warming Swindle*, March 2007), "The Press come to me and say, 'show us the greenhouse disaster'. I say to them, 'there is none'".

The Antarctic is getting colder, but there are local reasons which are partly responsible: Antarctica is cut off from the rest of the globe by the southern oceans. These oceans are referred to as the 'Roaring Forties', 'Furious Fifties' and 'Screaming Sixties' by mariners. The weather phenomena there are interesting: for example, only in the Antarctic is low-level cloud cover warming rather than cooling.

The melting of sea ice has no influence whatever on ocean levels; in fact, if Arctic ocean temperatures were to rise by a few degrees, ocean levels would *fall* slightly because water is most dense at 4°C.

Warmer ocean temperatures also result in more evaporation which, again, *reduce* ocean levels. The result of the evaporation is that quite a proportion falls as snow on high ground or on glaciers and in the Arctic and Antarctic where it stays as ice.

2. Global Warming will cause more extreme weather events, such as hurricanes and tornadoes and that this is already happening.
WRONG.

There will always be, as there always have been, extreme weather events—this is how the atmosphere 'does business'. However, dynamic meteorology suggests that warming will slightly reduce their intensity.

Richard Lindzen, Professor of Atmospheric Science at the Massachusetts Institute of Technology, states as follows:

> That the promotion of alarm does not follow from the science, is clearly illustrated by the following example.
> According to any textbook on dynamic meteorology, one may reasonably conclude that in a warmer world, extratropical storminess and weather variability will actually decrease. The reasoning is as follows. Judging by historical climate change, changes are greater in high latitudes than in the tropics. Thus, in a warmer world, we would expect that the temperature difference between high and low latitudes would diminish. However, it is precisely this difference that gives rise to extratropical large-scale weather disturbances. Moreover, when in

Boston on a winter day we experience unusual warmth, it is because the wind is blowing from the south.

Similarly, when we experience unusual cold, it is generally because the wind is blowing from the north. The possible extent of these extremes is, not surprisingly, determined by how warm low latitudes are and how cold high latitudes are. Given that we expect that high latitudes will warm much more than low latitudes in a warmer climate, the difference is expected to diminish, leading to less variance.

Nevertheless, we are told by advocates and the media that exactly the opposite is the case, and that, moreover, the models predict this (which, to their credit, they do not) and that the basic agreement discussed earlier signifies scientific agreement on this matter as well. Clearly more storms and greater extremes are regarded as more alarming than the opposite. Thus, the opposite of our current understanding is invoked in order to promote public concern.

Is there a basis for global warming alarm? Prof. R. Lindzen,
October 2005

That this is not happening is easily shown by two examples: that of hurricane strikes and tornadoes. These are well documented over the last 100 years and 50 years respectively in the USA and can serve to illustrate the point:

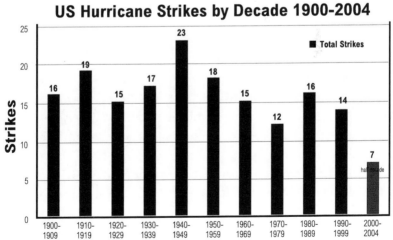

US Hurricane Strikes by Decade 1900-2004

Source: http://www.nhc.noaa.gov/pastdec.shtml

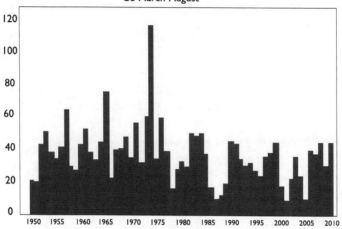

Number of Strong-to-violent [F3-F5] Tornadoes
US March-August

Evidence supporting 'colder = more severe weather' comes from an earlier century: careful analysis of the ships' logs of the British Navy based in the Caribbean between 1701 and 1750 (during the latter part of the Little Ice Age) have shown there were three times as many major hurricanes per year than between 1950 and 1998.

Much was made by Al Gore of Hurricane *Katrina* which devastated New Orleans as being proof of the terrors of Global Warming, but he is quite mistaken: *Katrina* was only a category 3 hurricane (really bad ones are category 5), but it tragically hit a bull's eye.

Many alarmists confuse the *cost* (in terms of real estate damage etc.) of a hurricane or a tornado with its *severity*. Modern coastal developments are very expensive to rebuild after storm damage, but that is hardly proof of severity, just of the stupidity of people building in areas where severe weather frequently causes serious damage.

3. There will be a serious shortage of water. WRONG.

The effects of global warming are not evenly distributed when they occur (as Lindzen pointed out above). In the tropics temperatures rise less, but rainfall increases, as is likely to be the case in some extra-tropical areas as well. Not everywhere will gain, of course: climate is

134

not designed to suit everyone's whims and requirements—changes in climate (for whatever reason) has winners and losers, but overall a warmer climate will mean more fresh water, not less.

In this connection it shows how Global Warmists will use *any* weather to claim that it is caused by man-made global warming—flooding is also blamed on 'global warming'.

4. Tropical diseases, such as malaria, will spread. WRONG.

Once again the IPCC seems determined, as is Al Gore, to spread alarm and disinformation. The group that put together the idea that malaria would spread north had only two real experts on vector-borne diseases. These two found themselves constantly at loggerheads with the rest of the group, none of whom had the slightest expertise in the area, but all of whom were activists in environmental movements. One member's 'expertise' was a paper on crash helmet design and his only other claim to fame were alarmist papers on the dangers of mobile phones! One of the two real experts, Prof. Paul Reiter of the Pasteur Institute in Paris, eventually resigned from the IPCC. He then found they continued to use his name as supporting their erroneous conclusions. Only after having to threaten legal action was his name removed.

Incidentally, this misuse of names by the IPCC is nothing unusual. The boasted '2500 scientists' of the 2006 report turned out to be about sixty scientists—most of whom were also activists.*

* Much is frequently made of a supposed 'consensus' among scientists. Scientific knowledge is never about consensus, it is about evidence, experiments, deductions and rational conclusions tempered by scepticism. Both 'sides' can claim vast numbers of supporters, but this is not relevant to the debate. The world had a consensus in the time of Noah: Noah was right the rest were wrong! The world had a consensus that the earth was flat, that the sun went round the earth, that atoms were indivisible; the list is endless.

Malaria itself is not a specifically tropical disease. One of the worst outbreaks of malaria was in Siberia in the 1920s. It has been endemic in Europe and America for millennia. It was only eradicated in the Fens in the 1950s and in Holland in the 1970s. Again, Al Gore makes much of this fear in his film. He claims Nairobi was originally built in a malaria-free area only to be infected as a result of global warming. This is incorrect. It was built as a base for the railway then being constructed into the Rift Valley. It was then a town riddled with malaria. Ironically, it is now virtually free of malaria!

The main cause of the spread of malaria is poverty. The very poor cannot afford the simple measures that could reduce or eradicate the disease: screens, better diet and use of insecticides and where necessary anti-malarial medicines. The effective banning of DDT after Rachel Carson published her novel, *Silent Spring*, has been a crime against humanity. The ban has resulted in about 40 million deaths so far: Hitler and even Stalin pale into insignificance.

5. The Gulf Stream will be overwhelmed by meltwater from Greenland and Europeans will freeze to death—due to Global Warming. WRONG.

This amusing suggestion (taken up in the film *The Day After Tomorrow*) is also espoused by Al Gore. The scare was started when a random measurement of the salinity of the ocean where the Gulf Stream flows seemed to show a serious dip in concentration. It turned out, after more regular monitoring was established, that this was just an error. The Gulf Stream sometimes shifts its position, pushed south by fluctuating cold currents coming down from Baffin Bay, the Davis Strait and the Sea of Labrador. It was just such a shift, in 1912, that caused an iceberg to drift too far south into the path of the *Titanic* on that terrible and tragic night of the 14th April.

Even the Super Computer models, about which more later, have failed to show that this could occur.

Greenland is not melting any faster than it has done for the last several thousand years. It is probable that the Gulf Stream was once overwhelmed by the bursting of a gigantic natural ice dam across half of America, unleashing a catastrophic amount of fresh water into the Atlantic (see graph at the bottom of page 143), but the whole of the Greenland icesheet could produce nothing like that amount of water.*

* Land-based ice mass: 90% in Antarctica (which is getting colder), 4% in Greenland and 6% in the rest of the world's mountains and glaciers.

6. There will be huge extinctions in the next 50 years. WRONG.

Paul Ehrlich, in 1981, predicted that by the year 2000 half of the earth's species would be extinct and all would be gone by 2015. Why anyone should go on listening to such a person after that remains baffling, but they do.

The trouble is that these figures were simply plucked out of the air. Norman Myers, author of *The Sinking Ark* (1979), started this particular scare. His argument was bizarre. He asserted that until 1900 one species went extinct every four years. Then, quoting a 1974 conference in which a 'guess was hazarded' that extinction rates had reached 100 a year, he arbitrarily decided that this figure was still too low. He suggested that 100 species a *day* would be a better figure or about 40,000 a year or 1 million in 25 years. And that is the whole basis for the scare. It starts with an estimate and then this is multiplied by 160,000 and we are told we face disaster. It makes for good headlines, of course, and lots of funds for environmental organisations.

The reality is very different. It is true that species do go extinct and that man can be the cause of some of these extinctions, but there is no evidence that any extinctions have been caused by 'climate change' in the last four centuries. No-one has the slightest idea how many species exist on the earth anyway. Estimates vary from 3 million to 80 million. If we take the lowest estimate, then over 80% of the species are insects; if the higher estimate, then over 98% would be insects. Deciding if a species smaller than a human fingernail has become extinct presents almost insuperable difficulties—how can we possibly search every square inch of the globe to check if a particular small insect does not exist any more? We would notice if whales or polar bears disappeared (there is no danger of that by the way), but not if a tiny insect or an amoeba had disappeared.

7. Global Warming will cause mass starvation. WRONG.

This is partly reliant on baseless fear no. 3 above. As with any climate variation, some parts of the globe will get warmer and possibly drier; others will get warmer and wetter. With the increase in both warmth and CO_2, however, the overall picture is very rosy. Even the

IPCC admits that an increase in temperature between 2° and 3°C would increase harvests and yields. Satellite measurements over the last three decades have shown a 4% per decade increase in biomass. Incidentally, CO_2, as well as being a general fertilizer helps plants take up water more efficiently—a double bonus as far as water supplies are concerned in a warmer world. As the higher latitudes warm more than the tropics, vast tracts of land in the northern hemisphere, which are currently too cold, would become available for cultivation.

That starvation is mainly caused by human activity is true enough: war, poverty, bad government and incompetence. In the last fifty years remarkable strides have been made in agriculture. The Green Revolution* was begun in the late 1940s under the influence of Norman Borlaug. Use of this agro-technology tripled yields across Europe and Asia. As a result, although the planet's population has doubled in sixty years from 3 billion to 6 billion, less people are starving today than fifty years ago. However, the Green Revolution has probably reached its zenith and further developments will be needed to ensure that the situation improves. GM (Genetically Modified) crops will certainly provide part of the way forward, but any genuine warming will be a very welcome boost to agricultural output. The Western neurotic concern with 'organic farming', if fully implemented, *would* cause mass starvation in very short order. Organic farming produces only half the yield of orthodox agriculture and there really is not enough virgin land available to double the amount needed for agricultural use. As the distinguished Indian plant biologist C. S. Prakash put it:

Organic farming is sustainable. It sustains poverty and malnutrition.

*nothing whatever to do with the Green Party or Greenpeace.

8. Carbon dioxide levels will go on rising indefinitely. WRONG.

Although CO_2 levels may well go on rising for some time, there are important limiting factors.

As long as the oceans are warming then the reservoir of dissolved CO_2 in them will tend to diminish leading to rising atmospheric CO_2 levels. However it has been discovered that there is a definite limit to how warm oceans can get. Total ocean warming is driven by surface ocean temperatures. The sun warms the surface, but heat transference downwards is very very slow: water is a very poor conductor of heat and convection tends to keep warm water on the surface. The deep oceans hardly warm at all. Observations of surface ocean temperatures had long shown that there was a limit to how warm they could become. The cut-off temperature is around 29.5°C. In 2001 a most interesting discovery was announced to explain how this limit was controlled: the Pacific Ocean Heat Vent. Study of data from Japan's GMS-5 geostationary satellite over the Pacific Ocean showed how the earth has this extra means of losing heat into space—like a huge safety valve; a quite remarkable phenomenon, but apparently still unknown and certainly not predicted in Greenhouse circles. It shows that the release of CO_2 would slow down and stop, even if temperatures generally rose.

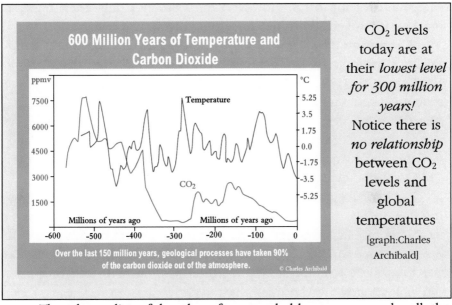

600 Million Years of Temperature and Carbon Dioxide

Over the last 150 million years, geological processes have taken 90% of the carbon dioxide out of the atmosphere. © Charles Archibald

CO_2 levels today are at their *lowest level for 300 million years!* Notice there is *no relationship* between CO_2 levels and global temperatures

[graph:Charles Archibald]

The above list of baseless fears probably covers nearly all the horror scenarios constantly thrown at us by the IPCC, the European Union, politicians in general, the media and the activists. CO_2 levels are rising: this is good news. Temperatures may be modestly rising: this too is good news. But are the two connected as we are being led to believe?

The answer is no, but we need a little climate history to explain why. And then we need to ask if we do know what does cause climate change.

What is really going on?

There are ways of estimating temperatures in the past which, though not as precise as using satellites or thermometers, give us a pretty good idea as to how warm or cold the past millennia have been compared to the present.

There are a range of indicators available. Some have relatively short-term use, others can be much longer term. There is not space to list all of them, but I will outline how just a few of them work.

Satellites are the most reliable method of measuring the overall temperature of the earth. However, their use has only been possible since the 1970s and so can tell us nothing before that date.

Thermometers: from 1880, when relatively consistent temperature records were kept in reasonably representative parts of the world, eg the USA or Europe, averages are attempted from these records. Since there were no thermometers at the Poles, as no-one had gone there, averages near the start of records are not very reliable. As we saw above, GISS itself is none too reliable in its analysis of the data.

Before that date use is made of what are called 'proxi' ('standing in for' a thermometer) measurements.

Agriculture in mountainous terrain, eg in the Alps or Himalayas. How far up the mountain sides ancient farmers grew certain crops or trees grew gives a very useful indicator of how warm or cold the earth was at the time. Archaeologists can study buried remnants of plants and trees to produce a temperature proxi from how far north certain species were able to grow.

Grape vines grew even in Southern Scotland during the Roman Warm Period, which shows how warm it was compared to today. Just exactly how much warmer in terms of degrees is not possible to measure.

Tree rings are not so useful for temperatures. Trees grow in the summer and not the winter and how much they grow is not only a factor of temperature but also how much rain there has been and how much CO_2 there is in the atmosphere. A warm summer with plenty of rain may be followed by a very cold winter which the tree ring would not record. Misuse of tree ring data is what scuppered Dr Michael Mann's infamous 'Hockey stick'.

Ice cores are excellent long-term indicators of both temperature and atmospheric content (eg how much CO_2 etc.) and a good measure of 'proxi' temperature is in the oxygen-18 content of the ice (H_2O) and the air bubbles trapped in it.

Normally oxygen has an atomic weight of 16, but there is a heavy oxygen isotope with an atomic weight of 18. This heavy oxygen makes water heavier and slightly more sluggish and the amount of ^{18}O compared to ^{16}O (normal) in an ice sample tells us how warm or cool the oceans were when the vapour from them turned into snow and fell onto the area producing the icesheet. If the water was cool then less ^{18}O water becomes vapour compared to the lighter ^{16}O water. The ice formed at that time would tell us that the oceans were cool.

Ice cores can take temperatures back several hundred thousand years.

Uptake of Oxygen-18 can be used from the remains of living things as well. Sea sediments formed by the slow accumulation of dead organisms can give a good idea of sea temperatures over long periods of time—these have the added advantage of helping to smooth out temperature fluctuations over these long periods as seas and oceans warm and cool only very slowly.

Analysis of ice cores taken from both the Arctic and the Antarctic go back some 600,000 years. The analysis reveals both the temperature (from ^{18}O) and the make-up of the atmosphere at the time from pockets of air trapped in the ice. Initial results seemed to indicate a very close relationship between CO_2 levels and temperature: as the CO_2 levels went up, so did the temperature. Much was made of this in Al Gore's film, *An Inconvenient Truth*. However, the initial results were based on samples taken at least 1000 years apart in the core. Since then much more detailed analysis has been made which revealed that, though rising temperatures and rising CO_2 levels did seem related, there was a significant delay (several hundred years) in the start of CO_2 rise after the temperature rose. In other words, CO_2 rises were caused by the temperature rise, not the other way round! This is not very surprising, as the rise in CO_2 comes from the gas being discharged from warming oceans which respond much more slowly to temperature rises than the land does. The importance of this result cannot be overstated: it removes the *only* piece of observational evidence claimed for the Greenhouse hypothesis. The current rise in CO_2 is more than likely due to the Medieval Warm Period and only partly to do with modern industrial output.

Finally, Oxygen-18 is taken up into the shells of sea creatures which have been living and dying in the sea for hundreds of millions of years. From this, proxi temperatures can be taken back to the beginning of the Phanerozoic era nearly 600 million years ago. These last temperature proxis are not giving day to day fluctuations, of course, just trends over millennia.

Studies of these proxis can now present us with trends over huge periods of time and these results I will now reproduce:

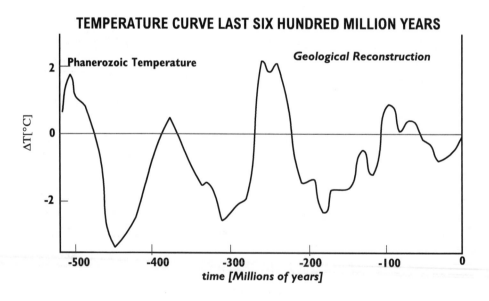

142

TEMPERATURE CURVE LAST SIX MILLION YEARS
Oxygen isotope ratio ^{16}O to ^{18}O

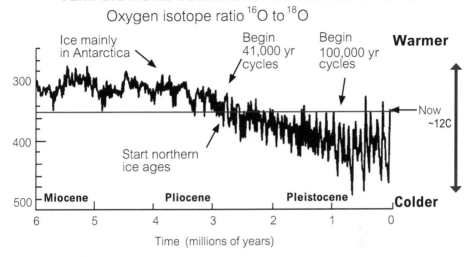

TEMPERATURE CURVE LAST FIFTEEN THOUSAND YEARS

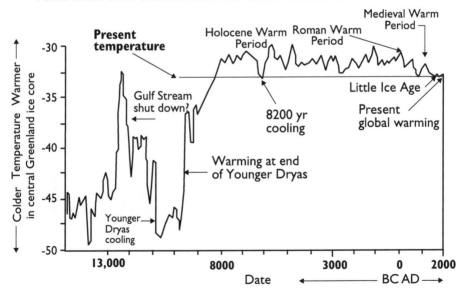

TEMPERATURE CURVE LAST THOUSAND YEARS
(based on work by Prof. Hubert Lamb)

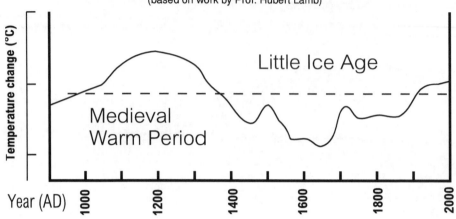

Global Temperature 1880-2007

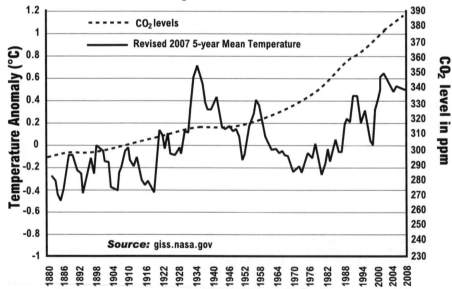

With this overview it becomes apparent that temperature fluctuations are quite normal. Although the 'rhythms' are not precise they can be traced and connected to long term natural phenomena. These can be identified as follows:

A. Solar:
1. 25-36 days: the rotation of the sun on its axis*
2. 11 & 22 year sunspot cycle†—the sun's magnetic field reverses after each 11 year cycle at the solar maximum, so it's about 22 years before it's back to where it was.
3. 87 year Gleissberg cycle‡
4. 210 year De Vreis-Suess cycle‡
5. 1500 year Bond-Dansgaard-Oeschger cycle‡

* Rotation of the sun is fastest at the equator and slowest at the poles as the sun is not a solid.
† This cycle can vary from 9-17 years.
‡ We really do not know if these cycles are long term or merely superficial regularities. The sun remains an 'unpredictable beast'!

These are all based on detected variations in the sun's activity over time.

Then to these cycles can be added those that result from variations in the earth's orbit around the sun.

B. Earth/Solar (Milankovitch rhythms):
6. Elliptical variation of orbit—100,000 years
7. Tilt variation—41,000 years
8. Precession of axis of spin—23,000 years

C. Galactic:
9. 32 million year cycle
10. Then, on top of all the above is a very slow rhythm of around 140 million years detected by Jewish astrophysicist Nir Shaviv and confirmed by paleogeologist Jan Veizer.

All these cycles (and there may be others), some more regular than others, interact with each other over the millennia like instruments in an orchestra, sometimes reinforcing each other, sometimes subtracting from each other, operating at different strengths and time periods, causing major 'ice-ball' events and less dramatic ice ages over millions of years.

We will look at these three sets in order.

Solar:

The sun, our nearest star, has only in recent decades been properly investigated. Study of it requires very specialised instruments because of the massive output of energy they need to survive!

The sun is a huge 'thermonuclear device', 800,000 miles across (for comparison the earth is just 8000 miles across). The outer surface has a temperature of a mere 6000°C, but as you go beneath the surface temperatures reach several million degrees, where nuclear fusion proceeds apace. It is a raging inferno shooting out flares and mass ejections of plasma into the solar system. It also puts out something called the solar wind. This is in effect a kind of solar atmosphere blowing out from the sun in all directions and reaching well beyond the orbit of the outermost planet Neptune (and well beyond Pluto, now demoted from planethood!). The solar wind's existence was only confirmed by observations in the early seventies.

In its youth the sun was paradoxically less bright than today, giving out only 70% of its current energy. However, its magnetic field and solar wind was probably much greater. This is just as well because otherwise the earth might have permanently frozen solid.

It still has a massive magnetic field which bends, twists and fluctuates in intensity: sunspots, darker blotches which can be observed on the surface with a simple telescope (by projecting the image onto a screen—*never* look at the sun directly), indicate periods of high intensity. These are indicated by rhythms A 1-3. However, they are not very predictable: the sun has had periods of 'going to sleep' in terms of sunspots, also times when the sunspot cycles speed up or slow down.

Sunspots have been pretty consistently observed since the time of Galileo and a nearly complete record exists of sunspot counts from that period to the present day. In the late 19th century an astronomer called Maunder carefully drew together all the data and made an interesting but somewhat mysterious discovery. Below is a barchart of the sunspot data:

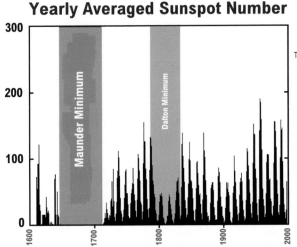

Yearly Averaged Sunspot Number

The Dalton Minimum ran from 1790-1830
It was similar to the Maunder Minimum
but less severe.

The 'Maunder minimum' band running from about 1640-1720 represents a period when no sunspots were observed—the sun 'went to sleep'.

Incidentally, you can see traces of the three rhythms in this barchart, the eleven year, 80 year and 210 year cycles (A.4).

The significance of the Maunder minimum will become clearer later on.

A.5. 1500 year Bond-Dansgaard-Oeschger cycle.

The discovery of this rhythm is much more recent. It is a rhythm of rising and falling global temperatures. It appears to be very persistent, going through ice ages and warm periods. Again, like the sunspots, the rhythm is not exact and in fact can vary as much as ±500 years—but it is clearly a rhythm nonetheless. There have been at least two warm periods in historical times: The Roman Warm Period, the Medieval Warm Period and possibly our current warm period. These were preceded by the Holocene Warm Period.

Its existence was established by the painstaking work of several research groups led by those named. Bond traced the past movement of icebergs moving south into the Atlantic. Icebergs are huge chunks of glaciers that make it to the sea, break off and float slowly with the ocean current, melting as they drift south. How far south they reach before melting completely is determined by how warm or cold the planet is, particularly the oceans. Icebergs leave a trace of their existence by rafting the rock gravel they chiselled up when they were part of a glacier.

When they finally melt, they drop this rocky signature onto the ocean floor. By examining the rock content and the latitude of this sediment, a picture of where the gravel came from and when it was dropped can be built up. This is what Bond and his co-workers did and they discovered this 1500 year cycle of the advance south and retreat north of the icebergs.

Dansgaard and Oeschger studied the ice cores of Greenland and found matching oscillations in the temperature, which tied up with more research on the Vostok Glacier ice core in Antarctica by the Russians and the French (Claude Lorius).

Similar work was done by Peter deMenocal (a colleague of Bond) off the coast of Africa, not with icebergs but with the remains of plankton whose populations and varieties depend on how warm or cold the oceans are. He found a pattern of wet and dry coinciding with the warm and cold fluctuations further north.

Whereas there has been no specific discovery of a corresponding rhythm of the sun—partly because such measurements would require a much longer period of time to observe—nonetheless, if the two cycles of 87 and 210 years are run together on a computer they form maxima (ie they reinforce each other) every 1470 years, nicely fitting this experimentally determined temperature rhythm and strongly suggesting than this 1500 year cycle is also solar driven.

B. Earth/Solar (Milankovitch rhythms):

In the 1920s a Serbian engineer and amateur astronomer, Milutin Milankovitch, refined the effect of the variations in the earth's orbit*, tilt

---

148 * based on the original work of James Croll, whose detailed theory appeared **CHAPTER 11**
in two books, *Climate and Time* (1875) & *Climate and Cosmology* (1885).

and precession to help explain the Ice Ages. He calculated the three rhythms:

- Elliptical variation of orbit—100,000 years: As the earth orbits the sun it is tugged by the gravity of the other planets which makes changes to the elliptical orbit around the sun, sometimes moving the earth away and sometimes nearer which naturally affects how much energy the earth receives from the sun, causing warming or cooling.

Added to this is:

- Tilt variation—41,000 years: the angle of the earth's tilt changes over time, again due to various gravitational tugs. This too will affect the angle of the sun's rays, again affecting the climate.
- Precession of the axis of spin—23,000 years: like a spinning top the earth precesses as it spins according to well understood laws of mechanics. This too will affect the angle of the sun's rays on the earth.

In passing, the moon's orbit plays a remarkable part in maintaining the earth's tilt. There was always the potential for the earth's axis to 'roll over' to lie horizontally (which has happened to Uranus)—with catastrophic effect. Half of the earth would freeze, the other half boil. The moon's orbit seems designed to prevent this ('seems designed?' Heaven forfend!).

Geological evidence has confirmed the effects of these rhythms on the climate, but nonetheless, although in many instances the coolings took place as predicted, there were times when they did not occur, strongly suggesting that there are other factors which can over-ride these effects.

C. Galactic:

The sun with its solar system is part of the Milky Way, a Galaxy (from the Greek word *gala*, for milk) of perhaps several hundred billion other stars. As far as we know our galaxy (one of an estimated 50 billion galaxies) has the form of a flat spiral with several arms radiating out from a central hub. The whole galaxy rotates like a Catherine Wheel, the arms trailing round in arcs. The hub is raised above and below the flat spread of the arms and is a dense mass of stars and gas. The whole galaxy ripples with magnetic and gravitational fields of varying intensities depending on whereabouts in the galaxy you look. The earth, fortunately, is currently well out between spiral arms and not near the centre where radiation levels (particularly the dangerous radiations such as gamma rays, X-rays and ultraviolet) would destroy all life on this planet. The galaxy is also being riddled with cosmic radiation. Cosmic radiation is a slight misnomer as it is not electromagnetic radiation like X-rays or light, but fragments of atoms, protons, electrons etc. travelling at incredible speeds, but seldom in straight lines, because, being charged particles, they follow the tortuous magnetic fields that twist and turn throughout the galaxy. They are the 'shrapnel' from exploding stars (supernova) within our galaxy (and just occasionally from another galaxy). The importance of cosmic rays will become clear later on.

The stars moving within the Galaxy do not hold the same position like soldiers on parade, but rather wander under the influence of the variable gravitational field in the 'locality' produced by other groups of stars. Over millions of years the sun along with planets has wandered between several of the spiral arms within the galaxy and also, rather like a dolphin, it leaps up and down above and below the plane of the 'wheel' of the galaxy: the frequency of this leaping and plunging is the 32 million year cycle. Then, lastly, we move between the spiral arms in a very slow rhythm of around 140 million years. These movements through the Galaxy were worked out by the Jewish astrophysicist Nir Shaviv and confirmed by paleogeologist Jan Veizer through the remarkable effect this has had on very long-term climate trends on the earth (using ^{18}O in the shells of very ancient sea creatures).

When I consider your heavens,
the work of your fingers,
the moon and the stars,
which you have set in place,
what is man that you are mindful of him,
the son of man that you care for him?

Psalm 8:3-4

If we can now 'come back down to earth' after this space odyssey, all of these processes affect the climate of planet Earth. But how?

In the case of varying orbit and tilt the answer is relatively simple. Distance from the sun and angle of the sun's rays will diminish or increase the amount of solar energy received.

But what about sunspots? What about our wanderings through the Galaxy? This is not so simple.

Up until the 1970s it was speculated that the very slight variations in the sun's radiance might account for the fluctuations in average temperature over decades and centuries, but calculations strongly suggested that these variations were too small, somewhere around ±0.1%. At the time no-one could see how the effect of the sun's variations could be amplified, so the theory was put on the 'back-burner'.

It was just around this time that a new hypothesis came on the scene, which originated with a relatively obscure Swedish climate scientist, Bert Bolin. He suggested that the climate might warm because of the increasing amount of CO_2 being generated by human consumption of fossil fuels. Originally he proposed this as an optimistic possibility because temperatures had fallen for thirty years and the fear was of a new Ice Age approaching. Bolin's hypothesis suggested that the extra CO_2 just might help stave off this disastrous possibility.

Around 1970 global temperatures began to rise again. Fears of an Ice Age vanished. Then oil prices quadrupled almost overnight, in Britain the miners went on strike and politicians in the West were facing some difficult choices. In Europe the influence of the burgeoning 'environmental' lobbies and Green politicians was strong. The use of Proportional Representation (PR) in European elections gave undue influence to minority groups like the Greens.

In the UK Mrs Thatcher came to power determined to break the power of the unions, the NUM in particular. Energy needed to be secure. A lot of oil came from politically unstable countries and coal from her domestic enemies, the miners. She determined that nuclear power stations were the best way forward, but they were considered dangerous by environmental groups. Caught between a rock and a hard place, Mrs Thatcher reached for some 'moral high ground' and found it in the newly emerging Greenhouse hypothesis of Bert Bolin. She was persuaded of the urgency by Crispin Tickell, John Houghton (then chief executive at the MetOffice and a convinced greenhouse activist and, it would seem, a Christian concerned for our 'stewardship of the planet') and others.

Determined that Britain should lead the way in this new planetary emergency, Mrs Thatcher threw money into setting up a world-beating Computerised Climate Unit: the Hadley Centre. She gave money to the Royal Society to 'prove this stuff' (to quote science journalist Nigel Calder). The Royal Society took the money. In doing so it prostituted its science credentials to politics. In this area at least it ceased to be doing science—it had become merely 'activist'. As we noted earlier, the Royal Society's motto is 'On the word of no man'—meaning nothing should be believed just because someone says so. It should be tested to see if it is true or false. Maybe they felt that a *woman's* word was different?

As Nigel Calder put it in *The Manic Sun*,

> The last and most important question to ask, about the United Kingdom's special role in greenhouse diplomacy and its supporting science, was why the British government was so keen on it. What explained the greening of Prime Minister Margaret Thatcher? When she sketched her new policies to the Royal Society in September 1988, some listeners may have imagined that she had suddenly changed from the world's sharpest politician into just another concerned grandmother. That would have been a scurrilous misjudgement.

> The speech to the Royal Society was a step in a project that she had pursued for two years, and which was already well advanced. In the political background, Europe was making endless trouble about British pollution of fresh water, the beaches, the sea and the air. On the other hand, the idea that nations should resolve to curb their carbon dioxide emissions suited the United Kingdom exceptionally well, given the impending demise of the nation's coal industry and the Prime Minister's support for nuclear power.

> She set out to wrest the initiative in environmental matters from the European Commission, by making the greenhouse warming a global

issue, with the British not just at the table but in the chair. The French and Dutch governments wanted to evolve a common European policy on greenhouse gases but the British environment minister vetoed that. Instead, the United Nations and its specialized agencies found the British becoming hyperactive on unaccustomed subjects, and giving very practical support in creating the global apparatus of the Intergovernmental Panel on Climate Change.

In her memoirs Baroness Thatcher explained a more partisan consideration in her policy. The environmental lobby used the concern about global warming to attack capitalism, growth and industry. She wanted authority in the environmental debate 'to ensure a sense of proportion'. Leading the defence against green socialism would be science.

Sonja Boehmer-Christiansen, a science policy researcher in Brighton, England, analysed the British role in the intergovernmental exercise much more thoroughly than is attempted here. By a pleasing irony her own work was funded as one of the many spin-offs of British global climate change research. In a talk at an international relations conference in 1994, her conclusion minced no words.

"Britain achieved its goal of a seat at the table by creating the famous scientific consensus of the Intergovernmental Panel on Climate Change," Boehmer-Christiansen said. The trick was done, she thought, by "a negotiated agreement between scientific institutions largely competing with each other for scarce resources."

The Manic Sun, p.198

In the summer of 1988 James Hansen, the mentor of Al Gore, gave testimony before a US Senate hearing that global warming was almost certainly being caused by human carbon dioxide emissions. The hearing had been stage-managed by Al Gore. The day had been deliberately chosen as likely to be the hottest day of the year. The night before the hearing, all the windows had been opened so that the air conditioning would not work properly. Thus everyone was sweating as Hansen made his 'chilling' statements. These dirty tricks were publically admitted in 2007.

In 1990 came the Rio Earth Summit. Vaguely under the auspices of the UN, it was originally a gathering for environmental activists. But politicians, realising the electoral advantage of appearing to side with 'saving the planet' (and wary of the danger of not doing so), muscled in on the act and the great Global Warming band-wagon began to roll.

To cut a long story short, this resulted in the creation of the IPCC (Intergovernmental Panel on Climate Change) with the Hadley Centre, along with the Goddard Institute of Space Studies (GISS—a branch of NASA) and other prestigious research organisations feeding in data and research papers. The IPCC releases major reports every five years (1996, 2001, 2006) charting the progress of investigations into Global Warming in various areas: the effects of Global Warming on the climate, health, economics, development etc.

As a result of Bolin's contribution, he was appointed chairman of the IPCC until he retired in 1998. He was succeeded by Dr Rajendra Pachauri who, as a former railway engineer, has no qualifications in climate science. John Houghton (later Sir John Houghton) worked as co-chairman of the IPCC's working group. The IPCC has a habit of rewarding those who come up with the 'right' ideas with prestigious posts.

Governments in the developed world (including the USA) poured money into climate research. In the USA in the ten years from 1986 to 1996 grants jumped from $170 million to $2 billion, nearly a twelve-fold increase. This is a great deal of money and drew in many scientists and others who might not have shown much interest in climate before: hundreds of thousands of jobs world-wide now depend on this issue of Global Warming—from scientists and their assistants to government employees involved in anything from Public Relations to sustainability enforcement of various kinds—anything from recycling to low-energy light bulbs in homes. Even local councils employ 'climate officers'.

The Royal Society, compromised with political money handed out to them by the British government, now aids a PR firm to maintain the Global Warming doctrine. People are employed, it seems, to go to any important public meeting where man-made Climate Change is being discussed (or challenged) to try and ensure that 'heresy' is not permitted to be spoken—happily not always with uniform success.

154

Any research scientist working in a field even remotely concerned with climate found it hard to get a grant unless they included some reference to man-made global warming as an accepted 'fact'.

But was it a fact of science? For a couple of decades there was some apparently plausible evidence to at least give credence to the greenhouse hypothesis. Dr David Evans, formerly of the Australian Greenhouse Office, put the evidence before around 2000 as follows:

In the 1990s there were basically four pieces of evidence for blaming carbon emissions:

First. Carbon dioxide is a greenhouse gas. Yep, we proved that in a laboratory over a century ago.

Second. Global temperatures had been generally trending upward for a century and we are told that concentrations of atmospheric carbon have also been rising for a century. Correlation is not causation, but in a rough sense it looked like a fit.

Third. Ice core data, starting with the first cores from Vostok in 1985, allowed us to measure temperature and atmospheric carbon going back through several past global warming and cooling events. The data points were more than a thousand years apart, but atmospheric carbon and temperature moved in lock-step: it looked like atmospheric carbon controlled the earth's temperature! The importance of this evidence is hard to overstate—it was the vital, mind-changing clincher, and it forms the centrepiece of Al Gore's movie [*An Inconvenient Truth*].

Fourth. There were no other credible suspects for causing global warming. This piece of evidence is implicit and often overlooked, but it was pretty important.

These were the four pieces of evidence that convinced scientists and politicians in the 1990s to get serious about blaming carbon.

But starting in about 2000, the last three of these four pieces fell away or reversed. Let's revisit the four pieces.

First. Yes, carbon dioxide is still a greenhouse gas. That evidence did not change, but you cannot reliably extrapolate what happens in a glass container in a laboratory to the real atmosphere, which has many feedbacks, clouds, and an ocean with dissolved carbon dioxide underneath it.

Second. We now know that from 1940 to 1975 the earth cooled while atmospheric carbon increased. That 35 year non-correlation might be explained by global dimming, which was only discovered around 2000. Or it might not. Oddly enough, solar effects would predict a cooling over those same years.

Third. The temporal resolution of the ice core data improved, that is, the time between data points decreased. By 2003 we knew that in past global warmings, the temperature started increasing about 800 years before the atmospheric carbon concentrations started rising. Causality does not run in the direction we had assumed in 1999—it runs the opposite way!

Fourth. There is now a credible alternative suspect. In October 2006 Henrik Svensmark showed experimentally that cosmic rays can cause cloud formation. Clouds have a net cooling effect, but for the last three decades there have been fewer clouds than normal because the sun's magnetic field, which shields us from cosmic rays, has been stronger than usual. So the earth heated up. It's still too early to judge what fraction of global warming is caused by cosmic rays, but now we have another suspect.

There is now no observational evidence to support the notion that global warming is caused by carbon emissions. None. You would think that in over 20 years of intense investigation, after spending $50 billion of government money on climate change, we would have found something! The only current reasons for blaming carbon emissions are the predictions of climate models—which extrapolate a greenhouse effect from the laboratory into the atmosphere.

from: *Rehabilitating Carbon Dioxide*, a presentation to The Lavoisier Group's 2007 Workshop held in Melbourne on 29-30 June 2007. See www.nzclimatescience.net.

Computer Climate Models

The Climate models are run on super computers at the Met Office's Hadley Centre in association with the University of East Anglia's Climate Research Unit (UEA-CRU) and at GISS and several other places.

It is vital to bear in mind that computer modelling of climate is not giving scientific knowledge. Modelling is essentially speculating on a computer and the results are only as good as the parameters that are fed into them and the programming designed to run them. However 'good' they are, they are not scientific evidence of anything—not even deductions from evidence.

So just how good are these models? Frankly, they are worse than useless—despite the enormous cost of the kit and the programmers. They are the living example of the old computer programmers' saying, "Garbage in: garbage out."

How do we know? A computer program designed to predict future weather and climate is clearly difficult to test, particularly as the IPCC frequently refers to climate in 50 or 100 years time (sometimes even further in the future). Few of us will live to see if the predictions are correct. However, an obvious way to test out their ability to accurately model climate is to see how they fare in modelling the *past* climate over the last 100 years where there is reasonably good data with which to compare the results.

This has indeed been done and the IPCC published the results. Because the models rely on the idea that CO_2 is what is driving global temperatures, their results are extremely disappointing for the Global Warming fraternity. Let Prof. Richard Lindzen of MIT take up the story:

> This brings us, finally, to the issue of climate models. Essential to alarm is the fact that most current climate models predict a response to a doubling of CO_2 of about 4°C (which is much larger than what one expects the simple doubling of CO_2 to produce: ie, about 1°C). The reason for this is that in these models, the most important greenhouse substances, water vapor and clouds, act in such a way as to greatly amplify the response to anthropogenic greenhouse gases alone (ie, they act as what are called large positive feedbacks). However, as all assessments of the Intergovernmental Panel on Climate Change (IPCC) have stated (at least in the text – though not in the *Summaries for Policymakers*), the models simply fail to get clouds and water vapor right. We know this because in official model intercomparisons, all models fail miserably to replicate observed distributions of cloud cover. Thus, the model predictions are critically dependent on features that we know must be wrong.

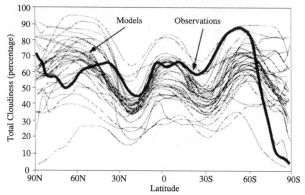

Figure 1. Each thin gray line shows an individual model's hindcast of percentage cloud cover averaged by latitude. The heavy black line shows the observed cloud cover.

Let me summarize the main points thus far:

1. It is NOT the level of CO_2 that is important, but rather the impact of man made greenhouse gases on climate.
2. Although we are far from the benchmark of doubled CO_2, climate forcing is already about ¾ of what we expect from such a doubling.
3. Even if we attribute all warming over the past century to man made greenhouse gases (which we have no basis for doing), the observed warming is only about 1/3-1/6 of what models project.

We are logically led to two possibilities:
1. Our models are greatly overestimating the sensitivity of climate to man made greenhouse gases, or
2. The models are correct, but there is some unknown process that has cancelled most of the warming.

Note that calling the unknown process "aerosols"* does not change this statement since aerosols and their impact are unknown to a factor of ten or more; indeed, even the sign is in doubt.

In arguing for climate alarmism, we are choosing the second possibility. Moreover, we are assuming that the unknown cancellation will soon cease.

The IPCC Third Annual Report made use of a peculiar exercise in curve fitting using results from the Hadley Centre.

* Aerosols are usually things such as smoke, or tiny liquid droplets   CHAPTER 11
produced in industrial smog and air pollution.

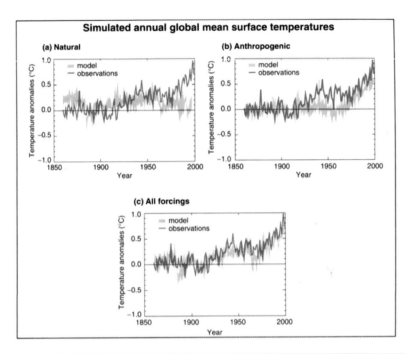

Simulated annual global mean surface temperatures

(a) Natural

(b) Anthropogenic

(c) All forcings

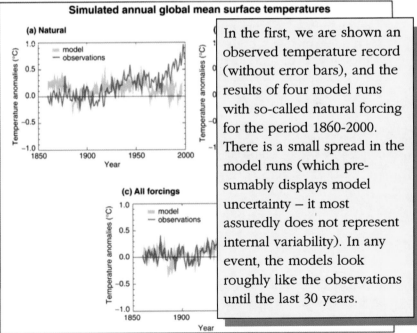

Simulated annual global mean surface temperatures

(a) Natural

(c) All forcings

In the first, we are shown an observed temperature record (without error bars), and the results of four model runs with so-called natural forcing for the period 1860-2000. There is a small spread in the model runs (which presumably displays model uncertainty – it most assuredly does not represent internal variability). In any event, the models look roughly like the observations until the last 30 years.

We are then shown a second diagram where the observed curve is reproduced, and the four models are run with anthropogenic forcing. Here we see rough agreement over the last 30 years, and poorer agreement in the earlier period.

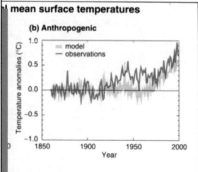

mean surface temperatures

(b) Anthropogenic

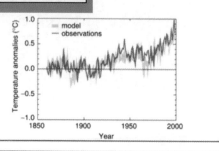

Simulated annual global mean surface temperatures

(a) Natural   **(b) Anthropogenic**

Finally, we are shown the observations and the model runs with both natural and anthropogenic forcing, and, *voilà*, there is rough agreement over the whole record. It should be noted that the models used had a relatively low sensitivity to a doubling of CO_2 of about 2.5°C.

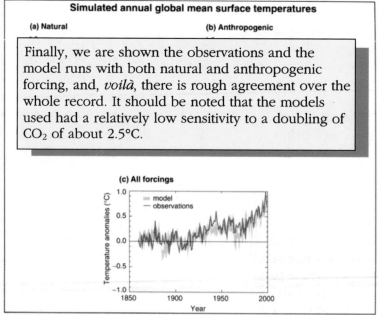

(c) All forcings

In order to know what to make of this exercise, one must know exactly what was done.

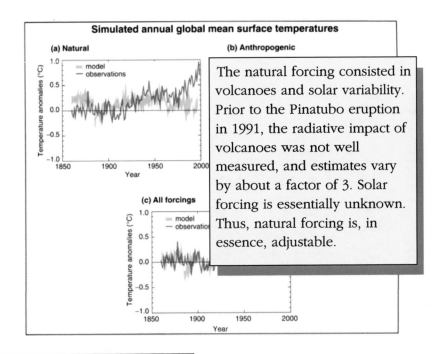

Simulated annual global mean surface temperatures

(a) Natural

(c) All forcings

The natural forcing consisted in volcanoes and solar variability. Prior to the Pinatubo eruption in 1991, the radiative impact of volcanoes was not well measured, and estimates vary by about a factor of 3. Solar forcing is essentially unknown. Thus, natural forcing is, in essence, adjustable.

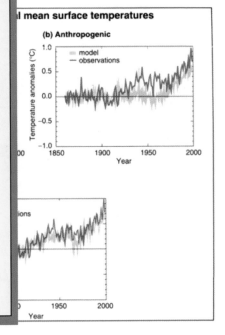

Anthropogenic forcing includes not only anthropogenic greenhouse gases, but also aerosols that act to cancel warming (*in the Hadley Centre results, aerosols and other factors cancelled two-thirds of the greenhouse forcing*).

Unfortunately, the properties of aerosols are largely unknown. In the present instance, therefore, aerosols constitute simply another adjustable parameter (indeed, both its magnitude and its time history are adjustable).

Science, 2003

Climate Forcing by Aerosols— a Hazy Picture

Theodore L. Anderson, Robert J. Charlson, Stephen E. Schwartz, Reto Knutti, Olivier Boucher, Henning Rodhe, Jost Heintzenberg

The global average surface temperature has risen by 0.6 K since the late 19th century. Ocean heat content has increased, and other climate indices also point to a warming world. Many studies have attributed this warming largely to top-of-atmosphere radiative forcing—a change in planetary heat balance between incoming solar radiation and outgoing infrared radiation—by anthropogenic greenhouse gases (GHGs) (1, 2).

Such attribution studies compare temperature observations to climate model simulations forced by various industrial-era agents. Among these agents, GHGs have well-constrained positive forcings (creating a warming influence) (1). In contrast, the mostly approximation that nonaerosol forcings are 2.7 W m⁻² (3, 4).

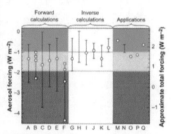

Uncertainties in aerosol forcings. Global-mean anthropogenic aerosol forcing over the industrial era (left axis) as estimated by forward (A to F) and inverse (G to L) calculations and as used in applications (M to Q) (20). Circles with error bars are central values and 95% confidence limits. Bare error bars are stated range. Squares represent specific forcing calculations using alternative formulations within the same study. Right axis: Total forcing over the industrial era using the approximation that nonaerosol forcings are 2.7 W m⁻² (3, 4).

> This was remarked upon in a recent paper in *Science*, wherein it was noted that the uncertainty was so great that estimating aerosol properties by tuning them to optimize agreement between models and observations (referred to as an inverse method) was probably as good as any other method, but that the use of such estimates to then test the models constituted a circular procedure.

> The choice of models with relatively low sensitivity, allowed adjustments that were not so extreme.

> New uncertainties are always entering the aerosol picture. Some are quite bizarre.

Cellular (and protein) particles injected into the atmosphere include fur fibres, dandruff, skin fragments, plant fragments, pollen, spores, bacteria, algae, fungi, viruses, protein "crystals", and more, ranging in size from tens of nanometers to millimeters.

BREVIA

Abundance of Cellular Material and Proteins in the Atmosphere

Ruprecht Jaenicke

Fig. 1. Observation of PBAPs greater than 0.2 μm in radius.

Of course this is the beauty of the global warming issue for many scientists. The issue deals with such small climate forcing and small temperature changes that it permits scientists to argue that everything and anything is important for climate.

In brief, the defense of the models starts by assuming the model is correct. One then attributes differences between the model behavior in the absence of external forcing, and observed changes in 'global mean temperature' to external forcing. Next one introduces 'natural' forcing and tries to obtain a 'best fit' to observations. If, finally, one is able to remove remaining discrepancies by introducing 'anthropogenic' forcing, we assert that the attribution of part of the observed change to the greenhouse component of 'anthropogenic' forcing must be correct.

Of course, model internal variability is not correct, and 'anthropogenic' forcing includes not only CO_2 but also aerosols, and the latter are unknown to a factor of 10-20 (and perhaps even sign). Finally, we have little quantitative knowledge of 'natural' forcing so this too is adjustable. Note that the Hadley Centre acknowledges that the "aerosols" cancelled most of the forcing from CO_2.

Yet, the 'argument' I have just presented is the basis for all popular claims that scientists now 'believe' that man is responsible for much of the observed warming!

It would appear that the current role of the scientist in the global warming issue is simply to defend the 'possibility' of ominous predictions so as to justify his 'belief'.

from: *Is there a basis for global warming alarm?*
Richard S. Lindzen, Alfred P. Sloan Professor of
Atmospheric Science, Massachusetts Institute of Technology,
Yale Center for the Study of Globalization, October 21st, 2005
[available as a pdf file from *rlindzen@mit.edu*]

So we can properly dismiss the Computer Models as being irrelevant. It is worth noting that the MetOffice record of accurate forecasting has deteriorated in recent years. Weather forecasts for even two days ahead are unreliable. Their Long Range Forecast for 2007 was,

"The summer in the UK was to be dry and warm/hot." Er: I think not! But as they rely on their CO_2-driven models it is not surprising that the results are so very poor. Attempts to obtain from them reasons why they support the CO_2 hypothesis resulted in failure: they could supply no science to support it.*

* On the MetOffice website, *www.metoffice.gov.uk/corporate/pressoffice/myths*, they even have a section, "five climate change myths", devoted to supposedly countering the facts as presented by the documentary *The Great Global Warming Swindle*. Sadly, all this has done is to expose astonishing scientific illiteracy. For example, Prof. John Mitchell FRS (the author) seems to think that cosmic rays are gamma rays; just one amongst a number of other scientific howlers on this page.

However, it is quite possible that in due time these flawed models could begin to quite accurately represent the climate—they contain so many adjustable assumptions (without experimental basis) that they may well hit the right 'formula' in time. However, what is so pathetic about this is that, because they may find the right alchemy of factors that seem to mirror reality, it is therefore assumed that the models are true pictures of reality. This is not science but science-fiction.

Keeping up the alarmist hype would indeed seem to be their intention. In their voluminous reports the IPCC often covers up or elides over uncomfortable real science. In 1996, for example, the politicians, NGOs and civil servants rewrote several of the conclusions (or *lack of* conclusions) reached by scientists, after the scientists left the conference, essentially reversing them.

Prof. Frederick Seitz, former President of the American National Academy of Science, stated regarding the 1996 report, "I have never witnessed a more disturbing corruption of the peer review process than the events that led to this IPCC report."

In *Unstoppable Global Warming*, Singer & Avery wrote:

Climate is so complex and variable that it's difficult to distinguish the causes of its variations. The technique adopted by the IPCC for its 1996 report was called "fingerprinting". The IPCC compared the detailed geographic patterns of climate change with the calculations of the climate models. This comparison, as published in the IPCC's Second Assessment in 1996, seemed to indicate a growing

164

correspondence between real-world observation and modeled patterns.

On examination, however, this result proved to be false. The correspondence is produced only for the time interval 1943 to 1970. More recent decades show no such correspondence. Nor does the complete record, which dated from 1905 to 1995. The IPCC claim is based on selective data. Under the rules of science, this cancels the IPCC's claim of having found a human impact on climate.

The IPCC's defenders claim that the crucial chapter 8 of the panel's 1996 report was based on 130 peer-reviewed science studies. Actually, the chapter was based mainly on two research papers by its lead author, Ben Santer, of the U.S. government's Lawrence Livermore National Laboratory. Neither of the Santer papers had been published at the time the chapter was under review and had not been subject to peer review. Scientific reviewers subsequently learned that both the Santer papers shared the same defect as the IPCC's chapter 8: Their "linear upward trend" occurs only from 1943 to 1970.

In fact, the IPCC report itself documented the reality that the human-made warming claim was false. The "fingerprint test", as displayed in figure 8.10b of the 1996 report, shows the pattern correlation between observations and climate models decreasing during the major surge of surface temperature warming that occurred between 1920 and 1940.

The IPCC's 1996 report was reviewed by its consulting scientists in late 1995. The "Summary for Policy Makers" was approved in December, and the full report, including chapter 8, was accepted. However, after the printed report appeared in May 1996, the scientific reviewers discovered that major changes had been made "in the back room" after they had signed off on the science chapter's contents. Santer, despite the shortcomings of the scientific evidence, had inserted a strong endorsement of man-made warming in the 1996 report's chapter 8:

"There is evidence of an emerging pattern of climate response to forcing by greenhouse gases and sulfate aerosols... from the geographical, seasonal and vertical patterns of temperature change.... These results point toward a human influence on global climate."

Santer added the following sentence to the crucial chapter 8 (of which he was the IPCC-appointed lead author) of the printed version of the 1996 IPCC report:

"The body of statistical evidence in chapter 8, when examined in the context of our physical understanding of the climate system, now points to a discernible human influence on the global climate."

Santer also deleted these key statements from the expert-approved chapter 8 draft:

• "None of the studies cited above has shown clear evidence that we can attribute the observed [climate] changes to the specific cause of increases in greenhouse gases."

• "While some of the pattern-base studies discussed here have claimed detection of a significant climate change, no study to date has positively attributed all or part [of the climate change observed] to [man-made] causes. Nor has any study quantified the magnitude of a greenhouse gas effect or aerosol effect in the observed data—an issue of primary relevance to policy makers."

pp. 62-63, Unstoppable Global Warming, Singer & Avery 2007

Returning to the 2001 report, the IPCC thought it had found new evidence for catastrophic global warming occurring. Dr Michael Mann released his 'Hockey Stick' graph.

1000 Years of Global Temperature Change

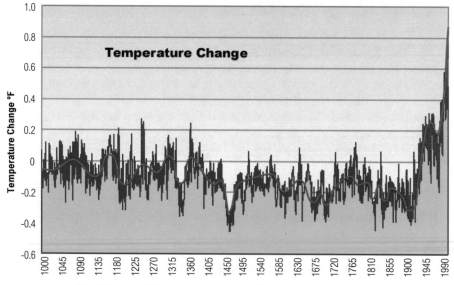

Dr Michael Mann's infamous 'Hockey Stick' graph

This did away with any suggestion of a Medieval Warm Period or of a Little Ice Age and was music to the ears of the IPCC. Gone were the embarrassing previous warm periods—wiped out at a stroke. Instead, here was a fearsome appearance of imminent disaster as temperatures are seen to be shooting up over the last hundred years. The IPCC were so impressed with this research that Michael Mann was put in overall charge of the main working group on climate change. The graph became iconic for activists around the world.

Unfortunately, Mann's paper had never been properly reviewed (scientifically unpardonable). When other scientists began to examine it, firstly they had great difficulty eliciting from Mann his research data and even more difficulty eliciting the computer algorithm used to create the graph.

When eventually these were examined (again by Steve McIntyre and Prof. Ross McKitrick), it was found that his computer program would generate a hockey stick from any set of random data—even a list of telephone numbers! Then it was discovered that he had relied on tree rings from the Bristlecone pine; tree rings are not a reliable temperature proxi and he had overlooked a crucial matter: that the rise in CO_2 caused a growth spurt in the few trees he examined—hence the apparent rapid rise in temperature over the last hundred years!

After these serious errors had been accounted for and his data re-run using proper maths, the old Medieval Warm Period and the Little Ice Age reappeared as before.

By the 2006 report the Hockey Stick graph had mysteriously disappeared without even an apology from the IPCC. But the myth of a supposed fingerprint continued to hold sway in the *Summary for Policy Makers*.

In 2008 Mann tried again with supposedly new data sets to generate his Hockey Stick. It was shown that he had simply rejected any data which showed the Medieval Warm Period and the Little Ice Age and that he was still using his faulty computer algorithm.

It is now firmly fixed in the public psyche that Man-made Climate Change is an established fact of science, despite the fact that there is no scientific evidence for it.

Coup de Grâce?

In July 2008 Dr Roy Spencer gave testimony before the US Senate. Dr Spencer is Science Team Leader for the National Aeronautic and Space Administration's collection of satellite temperature data and a principal research scientist at the University of Alabama at Huntsville's Earth System Science Center. Spencer told the US Senate Environment and Public Works Committee why the scientific data led him to conclude that global warming is not a crisis.

In his testimony he stated,

> "...in the last several weeks, we have stumbled upon clear and convincing observational evidence of particularly strong negative feedback (low climate sensitivity) from our latest and best satellite instruments." [details in *The Great Global Warming Blunder* by Roy W.Spencer, Encounter Books 2010]

In English this means that the overall climate system damps down any small effect CO_2 might have on temperature. All the super computer models assume the opposite because this makes the results alarmist. Put another way, it shows that all the research with computer modelling has been a complete waste of time and money. If the climate really did behave like the computer models then it would have 'crashed' many times in the past when CO_2 levels were twenty times what they are today.

CO_2 is purely beneficial and currently is at a relatively low concentration at 380ppm. There is no dangerous upper limit to worry about.* However, if it were to drop below 180ppm (as there is a risk of happening during a severe ice age) then most, if not all, vegetation would die off, leaving every creature on the planet starving to death.

---

* James Hansen's suggestion that 350ppm is the 'safe' limit is quite ridiculous as there is no such thing as an 'unsafe' level of CO_2. The higher it is, the better for humanity and the planet. To present any risk, CO_2 levels would need to be a *hundred times* greater than they are today.

But the Juggernaut grinds on as real science and real scientists are disregarded. No mention has been made in any news media of this clinching discovery by the Spencer team.

Chapter 12

The true cost in human lives

The real science of climate tells us that warming, if it is occurring, is something to be welcomed. If, as is just possible, we are entering another warm period like the Medieval Warm Period, then, on the weather front, we have very little to worry about. If, however, the sun decides to have another 'Maunder Minimum', then we may have good reason to worry, but in neither case can we as humans do anything about the weather, only try to adapt, as Joseph did in Egypt for the benefit of both Egypt and the wider human community.

Either way, misusing valuable resources to try and 'stabilise' the climate is the height of folly. Yet that at the moment is precisely what we are seeing our politicians, our governments, NGOs and, sadly, Christian relief agencies doing. The West can 'afford' to throw away its excess money if it so chooses—though in the current financial crisis it would seem to be the action of a suicidal lunatic—but the developing world cannot afford to do so.

If we in the West, urged on by such activists as George Monbiot, wish to revert to primitive conditions of living—intermittent electrical supply, severe rationing of fuel, organic farming—then so be it, but to condemn others to have to live in such wretched conditions is monstrous arrogance.

Let us get some facts straight

1. Letting people live in extreme poverty is an affront to God and is also the main cause of environmental degradation. Subsistence living is hand to mouth and cannot consider the effects of gathering wood or food today on the future of the land. Desperation leads to destruction of the environment. It is the wealthy nations that have cleaned up the environment so

that today the developed countries are the cleanest, safest (too safe in fact) and most ecologically well protected societies on earth and in all of history.

2. Carbon dioxide is not a pollutant but a life-giving gas, despite Barack Obama pledging to place it on the EPA's (Environmental Protection Agency) list of 'polluting' gases—in the same category as sulphur dioxide (SO_2) which causes acid rain, or dioxins which can be toxic.

Carbon dioxide is essential for all life on earth. Concentrations of CO_2 in the past have been up to twenty times higher than they are today and the planet flourished. To call it a pollutant is just ignorance.

It is quite amazing that the developed world is terrified, it seems, of a little warming (if we do get any more—temperatures have fallen since 1998) and even more terrified of this slight rise in CO_2. Warming is of net benefit to human beings: more crops, less water stress, less deaths from cold (currently running at five times as many as die from heat-related illnesses). More CO_2 is wholly beneficial.

Warming has also benefited animals which can be observed to spread further north (spreading south is not so easy as, of course, the southern hemisphere is predominantly ocean) without, it seems, displacing more northerly species. Polar bears are thriving now, except one group which is suffering through cold.

So why the hysteria? I put it down in part to Social Hypochondria. We all have a tendency to hypochondria, fearing that some ache or pain is a life-threatening disease. The more we are able to access a Health Service, the more doctors have to try and deal with it. Sometimes it is easier for them to simply prescribe a medicine even if the patient is not ill. This reinforces the hypochondria, leading, in rare cases, to the Howard Hughes syndrome (see Glossary p. 226).

What we see is whole societies in the rich and comfortable West succumbing to the condition. Every weather event becomes viewed as a symptom of apocalyptic disaster looming. The more it is taken seriously (often by people who should know better) the worse the condition gets until now we have nearly become like poor Howard Hughes.

The hypochondria itself would be bad enough, but the social effect has been to create a new Phariseeism. It is not enough to feel ill yourself; now this must be imposed on others—a true dog-in-manger situation.

Extremely restrictive rules are placed on everyone: the current obsession with 'Carbon Footprints' would be laughable if it was not so tragic.

39 Then the Lord said to him, "Now then, you Pharisees clean the outside of the cup and dish, but inside you are full of greed and wickedness.

40 "You foolish people! Did not the one who made the outside make the inside also? 41 But give what is inside [the dish] to the poor, and everything will be clean for you.

42 "Woe to you Pharisees, because you give God a tenth of your mint, rue and all other kinds of garden herbs, but you neglect justice and the love of God. You should have practised the latter without leaving the former undone.

43 "Woe to you Pharisees, because you love the most important seats in the synagogues and greetings in the market-places.

44 "Woe to you, because you are like unmarked graves, which men walk over without knowing it."

45 One of the experts in the law answered him, "Teacher, when you say these things, you insult us also."

46 Jesus replied, "And you experts in the law, woe to you, because you load people down with burdens they can hardly carry, and you yourselves will not lift one finger to help them."

Lk 11:39-46

The last verse is particularly relevant. For the people they lay these burdens on are not just people here in the West, but they do it to those in the developing world. We in the West can at least object; those in the developing world cannot.

They are told they must not use their fossil fuels, but use 'renewables'—solar and wind power. This is effectively to condemn them to not having electricity at all. Both these systems are very inefficient and extremely expensive. The West's love affair with wind energy is perhaps one of the silliest things in the history of technology.

The crass stupidity of building forests of these bird slicers; the huge cost to the taxpayer and the consumer, who is forced to pay the very high prices the power generated costs, then having to pay to build another coal, gas or nuclear power station to be available as permanent and immediate backup—as wind works for less that 25% of the time and seldom when peak demand requires it.

Why not just build the conventional power station? This would be far cheaper both to build and in cost to the consumer. It would do far less damage to the environment. We shall likely see the lights going out in Britain, Europe and the US anyway due to these crazy schemes. Britain will lose up to 30% of its generating power in the next five years as older power stations go off-line and are not being replaced.

But it is far, far worse for the developing nations, particularly those in Africa, the least developed continent. Asia has, on the whole, had the very good sense not to play ball with this Western hypochondria. China is bringing four coal-fired power stations on-line every week, thanks to a sensible plan some years back to try and get electricity to as many people as possible.

The same should be happening in Africa. Africa has both coal and oil and should be using it for the good of the people, but Western Governments and NGOs, Green Activists and Christian charities such as Christian Aid and TearFund, obsessed with greenhouse gas fears, are striving to prevent this happening.

"And you experts in the law, woe to you, because you load people down with burdens they can hardly carry, and you yourselves will not lift one finger to help them."

It is a sad state of affairs when Christians who raise money supposedly to try and help the destitute out of poverty are the very ones keeping them in it!

Those who are wise in this world can see the hypocrisy clearly. Michael Crichton, author of *State of Fear*, put the following remark in the mouth of one of his characters,

> "[Church leaders] promote '*What would Jesus drive?*'* As if they have forgotten that what Jesus would drive is the false prophets and fearmongers out of the temple!"

State of Fear, p.457

* A real-life 'Christian' green campaign in the USA.

But this has been a trend since the Green Movement went through a sea change from being a genuine lobby group, pressuring for industry to clean up its act and to protect the environment, to being a political activist group with strong post-marxist tendencies: green is the new red.

Within it were those who, rather childishly, believed in a past period when humans 'lived in harmony with nature' and to which they wanted the human race to return.

Thus, for them the developing world should not develop; they should remain in their 'harmony with nature' state. Industry is a curse, subsistence farming was 'harmonious' because it was 'organic'.

None of these eco-warriors have any real experience of 'living in harmony with nature'; if they had ever tried it they would quickly realise that there is no such experience to be had—that is if they survived long enough to tell the story. Most would be dead within a month. Maybe there is scope for a new TV programme, "I'm an eco-warrior. Get me out of here!"

To repeat C. S. Prakash's comment:

Organic farming is sustainable. It sustains poverty and malnutrition.

The Organic Farming Fashion

The obsession in the West with organic farming, even among Christians, who ought to have known better, is a spin-off from this kind of unreality.

The origin of organic farming lies in the anthroposophy of Rudolph Steiner, whose views on reality were distinctly bizarre: planting seeds in the right moonlight; believing that 'cosmic forces' entered animals, like cows or stags, through their horns. Thus the soil was to be nourished with cow horns stuffed with entrails. Christians ought to have been the first to reject such occult nonsense. The Soil Association believes this stuff, yet it is taken seriously by the BBC as if it were the fount of all knowledge, yet all is not what it seems.

Organic methods of ploughing and weeding are not good for the soil it claims to protect: killing earth worms and other organisms which hate being ploughed up. Modern low tillage techniques are far better for soil health. Their insistence on using manure (sometimes even human manure) is also a problem—there is a tendency for trace metals and other toxins to become concentrated in the soil. This poisoning of the soil was one factor that led to the abandonment of St. Kilda in 1930—incidentally, a very good example of a supposedly 'organic and sustainable society'. Yet the lives of the islanders were hard, unhealthy and short.

Even without the bizarre philosophy behind it, organic farming is a luxury that only the relatively wealthy in the West can afford. Yields from organic farming are up to 50% lower than conventional agriculture and the end products when eaten cannot be distinguished from conventional products: to look at they are often rather less appetising anyway. Yet people are foolish enough to pay more for the product. Why?

Well, they are told that they contain no dangerous chemicals which will give you cancer. Actually they do: many plants we eat naturally contain considerable quantities of dangerous chemicals— usually in amounts that are relatively harmless, but not always.

For example, kidney beans can be lethal if not properly cooked (*lectin* poisoning)—as vegetarians have occasionally discovered to their cost. Almonds contain *amygdalin,* which produces hydrogen cyanide when crushed or chewed. The herb basil contains the natural carcinogen *estragole*, which is hundreds of times more dangerous than the risk from pesticides.

Ordinary celery, organic or otherwise, contains ten times more carcinogens than the minute traces of pesticide found on conventional fruit or vegetables: a cup of 'organic' coffee fifty times more! The risks are small, of course, but not zero.

The relative risk of cancer from pesticides such as Lindane on conventional fruit and vegetables is around 0.000001%; from a cup of coffee is 0.1%; lettuce 0.04%; celery 0.004%. In other words, the pesticide risk is totally insignificant compared to naturally occurring risks.

However, not eating sufficient fresh fruit and vegetables can increase cancer risks generally by 20-30%.

If we are required to go organic, food costs will at least double: the poorest in the West will be unable to afford sufficient fresh fruit and vegetables and they will increase their risk of cancer by a very significant amount. Is that really a good trade off? And if the poor in the West will increase their risk, what of the destitute in the Third World for whom nuances of diet are out of the question? Anyway, they will die of the consequences of malnutrition long before cancer (in general a disease of older people) catches up with them. [See Lomborg, *the skeptical environmentalist* Pt V Ch.22 for a full examination of these cancer fears.]

Fifty to eighty years ago famines were the norm in Asia—yet today they are rare, even though the population in Asia has probably tripled. What happened to change the situation?

The Green Revolution

This Green Revolution has nothing whatever to do with Greenpeace or the Green Party. This revolution was begun in the late 1940s under the guiding influence of Norman Borlaug, working at the International Maize and Wheat Improvement Centre in Mexico City.

Using intensive farming techniques with fertiliser and pesticides, along with carefully selected crop varieties, yields across Europe and Asia more than tripled. For example, short-stalked wheat put more growth into the grain rather than the stalk and reduced the problem that occurs when the long-stalked varieties are flattened in severe weather and rot on the ground. Borlaug received the Nobel Peace Prize in 1970 for his work: a genuinely deserved award for a man who may well have saved a billion lives. Yet what happens today? Al Gore gets a Nobel Peace Prize for his fantasy film *An Inconvenient Truth* which, if its ideas were to be put into practice, would be likely to kill hundreds of millions of people.

Africa has not benefited as much from this revolution for a variety of reasons. The soil is ancient and relatively poor. Unfortunately, some governments are not stable, making wars and insurgencies only too common—ruining crops and driving the farmers off their land. Drought is also an ongoing problem.

However, the potential for Africa to experience its own Green revolution remains.

Biofuels

After wind power, biofuel is next in line to being the most absurd obsession of the West.

Scientifically speaking, it is simply attempting the age-old fantasy of perpetual motion.

Currently it takes the equivalent of six gallons of fuel to produce one gallon of biofuel. Improved processes may reduce this down to 3-4 gallons for one gallon of biofuel, but the laws of thermodynamics will not allow any better yields than that.

At the same time, growing crops for the purpose takes up huge tracts of agricultural land which should be available for growing food. Further, in the dash for cash from such crops, swathes of the rainforest are being torn up to grow them. It has to be said that even the activists are realising the absurdity of the idea. The EU, unfortunately, has not got even this level of understanding and has regulated that all fuel must contain a percentage of biofuel, thus perpetuating the scandal.

Frankenstein foods and Terminator genes

Genetically Modified (GM) crops may well help to bring a solution for Africa, providing a way can be found to persuade Africans that GM food is not dangerous. Unfortunately, due to the propaganda activities of NGOs with green agendas, many African governments have been told that GM crops will sterilise their women and cause all kinds of terrible diseases. As a result, even food aid needed urgently is rejected by some African countries because it contains GM corn. It seems they would rather see their people starve to death than accept 'Frankenstein food'. Yet the Americans have been eating it for nearly a generation without one single adverse effect. Organic produce really can kill people, and does from time to time. GM food has never killed anyone. Is it really likely that GM seed companies would knowingly and deliberately set out to poison their customers?

176

However, the state of fear induced by green activists over GM has placed these companies on the defensive; a situation they have not always managed very well. How can they when they have to counter lies at every turn by people who know only too well how to stir up the media and arouse the passions of the mob?

There is no doubt that it has been a clever propaganda campaign: the very term 'Frankenstein food' was a brilliant, if immoral, phrase. Similarly, the Terminator Gene—with its associations with horrific inhuman killing machines—has been used with unfortunate success. The idea behind the propaganda is that GM companies ensure that the seeds from the initial GM crop cannot be used for next year's crop because they are infertile. Aha! The poor peasant must pay for fresh seed from the GM company: exploitation!

The trouble is there is no truth to this. GM seeds are like all hybrid seeds that have been used worldwide in efficient agriculture (including 'organic' agriculture) for decades. The seeds will tend to revert to the original varieties from which the hybrid was crossed; only a proportion will grow true to the hybrid according to the straightforward laws of genetics discovered by Mendel. It *is* true that *theoretically* a terminator gene *could* be introduced—to prevent cross-fertilising in the wild. This has not been done in real life. All that exists is a patent. The company that owns the patent has made a solemn undertaking not to introduce such a gene into any GM food crop. In fact, this is the very thing so many activists paint as a terrible danger—escaping GM varieties causing mayhem in the wild. In other words, the critics are preventing the use of the very thing they had been asking for! But the activists don't want solutions, it seems. They want to *reduce* the human population, particularly the Third World population. They do not want to encourage it to grow more food and so flourish. What kind of twisted morality is this?

Yet GM crops have considerable potential to take over from the Green revolution which is beginning to peak.

Crops could be bred to resist drought better, or to grow in brackish water—irrigation has a long-term drawback of slowly introducing salt into the soil. Or to resist disease, reducing the need to spray the crop with pesticides—sometimes removing the need for any pesticides (something the green brigade should welcome, surely?). Or to include a vitamin precursor—as in the case of Golden Rice developed to include a vital precursor of vitamin A into the diet of poorly nourished children who might otherwise go blind. This strain of rice was developed by a GM company and then *given* away! OK, I am sure it was hoped that it might reap feel-good benefits towards the company, but is that so terribly wicked?

There is the possibility too of introducing vaccines against scourges like polio into the food, rather than relying on expensive medical vaccination campaigns which are difficult to conduct in backward areas of the world.

GM is not a magic cure to human ills, but it *is* a help, not a hindrance.

Down with people

Fears in the Western world about over-population are also exaggerated: future global population extrapolations increasingly suggest a peak around the year 2050 (the Lord tarrying) at about nine billion; down from earlier projections of 11 billion, though we must still be wary of extrapolations!

Yet we get persistent attempts to suggest that there are too many people. Sir Crispin Tickell, speaking on Radio 4 in 2008, stated that he thought human beings were like caterpillars, eating everything, and must be stopped. The UN has a programme of population reduction through a variety of means, not all of them ethical.

Having children is now beginning to be regarded as a potential waste of resources—bad for our carbon footprint. So much so that some people, who nonetheless seem to be able to speak to our government, have even stranger views. As Austin Williams states:

> Take Toni Vernelli, vegan campaign co-ordinator of the animal rights organisation, People for the Ethical Treatment of Animals (PETA), who explains that she had an abortion and sterilisation because, for her, 'every person who is born uses more food, more water, more

land, more fossil fuels, more trees and produces more rubbish, more pollution, more greenhouse gases, and adds to the problem of over-population.'

Now Vernelli is able to take guilt-free holidays to South Africa because, 'We feel we can have one long-haul flight a year, as we are vegan and childless, thereby greatly reducing our carbon footprint.'

Toni Vernelli quoted in Natasha Courtenay-Smith and Morag Turner, 'Meet the women who won't have babies—because they're not eco friendly', Daily Mail, 21st November 2007

from *The Enemies of Progress* by Austin Williams

This is truly sacrificing children to Molech (Lev 18:21, Lev 20:2-4).

Rachel Carson's *Silent Spring*

This book, published in 1962, has been unintentionally responsible for the deaths of between 30 and 50 million people (that's arguably more than the effect of *Mein Kampf* and *Das Capital* put together). Yet Carson, who died in 1964, was an earnest and well meaning lady.

She had seen the effect that insecticides could have on insects and, through their disappearance, on bird life. She prophesied a 'silent spring' when no birds sang as a result, in particular, of the use of DDT (Dichloro-Diphenyl-Trichloro-ethane).

DDT was first synthesised in 1874, but its pesticidal effects were not discovered until 1939. It proved remarkably effective and relatively safe to use. In particular, it was effective against the malarial mosquito: easy to apply, long lasting but harmless to humans.

However, as often happens, its enthusiastic use was sometimes overdone: in the early years it was used in agriculture by soaking seeds in DDT to prevent attack by pests—and it was very effective—however, as seeds were a very tempting morsel for bird life, it began to affect birds: it was thought (but with very little evidence) to soften their eggshells, leading to stillbirth hatchings. Clearly this might be unfortunate, but could have been easily cured by not soaking the seed in DDT, but spraying the growing crops at a later stage.

The hysteria caused by Carson's book, however, led to wild mythologies about DDT causing human cancer and being a deadly poison. Yet DDT could be eaten by humans with no ill effects and has never been shown to have any carcinogenic effect. But the result was an immediate ban on its agricultural use and, more importantly, an effective ban on its use as a malarial mosquito pesticide. Its use was suspended in many Third World countries (for fear of losing aid from the hyper-cautious First World) and the consequences have been horrific. Until this effective ban, the malarial mosquito was well on the way out. Malaria was ceasing to be a scourge in Africa and it too was beginning to look to be on its way out as a disease. Then spraying ceased or was much reduced and the result was three-fold:

1. Malaria re-emerged as a serious scourge. Deaths sky-rocketed and since its ban in the 1970s 30 to 40 million have died of malaria.

2. The malarial mosquito became tolerant of DDT (in a similar way as taking half a course of penicillin is more dangerous than taking none at all as the bacteria become resistant).

3. The substitutes were far more expensive, less effective and in addition *were* dangerous to human health—even in Britain the use of organo-phosphorous compounds (OPs) in sheep-dip have had serious health consequences for some farmers.*

* See Ch.15 'Licence to kill' in *Scared to Death*, C. Booker and R. North.

Now, too late, the value of DDT has been 'rediscovered' and it is being used. However, its effect is now far less potent.

Feel Good and Do Good

14 What good is it, my brothers, if a man claims to have faith but has no deeds? Can such faith save him?

15 Suppose a brother or sister is without clothes and daily food.

16 If one of you says to him, "Go, I wish you well; keep warm and well fed," but does nothing about his physical needs, what good is it?

17 In the same way, faith by itself, if it is not accompanied by action, is dead.

James 2:14-17

16 This is how we know what love is: Jesus Christ laid down his life for us. And we ought to lay down our lives for our brothers.

17 If anyone has material possessions and sees his brother in need but has no pity on him, how can the love of God be in him?

18 Dear children, let us not love with words or tongue but with actions and in truth.   1 Jn 3:16-18

Bjørn Lomborg is ex-Greenpeace and a Professor of Statistics. He was named one of the top 100 most influential people in the world by *Time* magazine. He started the 'Copenhagen Consensus', a conference of top economists who come together to prioritise the best solutions for the world's greatest material challenges.

Many mistakenly accuse Lomborg of a complacent optimism, but he writes:

Mankind's lot has actually improved in terms of practically every measurable indicator.

But note carefully what I am saying here: that by far the majority of indicators show that mankind's lot has *vastly improved*. This does not, however, mean that everything is *good enough*. The first statement refers to what the world looks like whereas the second refers to what it ought to look like. While on lecture tours I have discovered how vital it is to emphasize this distinction.

Lomborg, *the skeptical environmentalist*, p.4

In his recent book, *Cool It*, he summarises his argument about using resources wisely and effectively in the following extract.

An effort like Kyoto—which has spent much of the world's political will for the last decade, and which will cost $180 billion annually if concluded in full, yet yield surprisingly little benefit by the end of the century—shows the case [for effective solutions] clearly.

In Table 3 I have tried to compare the efficiency between Kyoto and a collection of smart policies—let us call them "feel good" and "do good" strategies, respectively. Of course, Kyoto could be tweaked and made better, but these are the proposals that are on the table, and in any case the differences are so huge and obvious that a better 'carbon cuts' proposal will only marginally change the individual entries and certainly not the outcome.

Table 3. The annual cost and efficiency of doing Kyoto or of doing a collection of smart strategies, with cost in parentheses

	Feel good (e.g. Kyoto)	Do good
Polar bears	0.06 saved	49 saved
Temperature deaths	84,000 more deaths	Already better
Flooding	$45 million in damage reduction	$60 billion damage reduction ($5b)
Hurricanes	0.6% damage reduction	250% damage reduction ($5b)
Malaria	70 million infections avoided	28 billion infections avoided ($3b)*
Poverty	1 million fewer	1 billion fewer
Starvation	2 million fewer	229 million fewer
Water stress	84 million more	Already better
HIV/AIDS	-	3.5 million lives saved ($7b)
Micronutrients	-	Avert 1 billion-plus malnourished ($3b)
Free trade	-	An extra $2.4 trillion annually
Drinking water & sanitation	-	Give 3 billion access ($4b)
Deal with climate effectively	-	$2/ton Carbon dioxide tax R&D for low-carbon energy ($25b)
PRICE TAG	**$180 billion/year**	**$52 billion/year**
		* individuals can be bitten many times

From *Cool It* by Bjørn Lomborg, page 226. Marshall Cavendish 2007

Michael Crichton's comments about Lomborg's book, *the skeptical environmentalist*, are interesting:

By now, many people know the story behind this text: the author, a Danish statistician and Greenpeace activist, set out to disprove the views of the late Julian Simon*, an economist who claimed that dire

---

* Julian Simon (1932-98), Professor of Economics, University of Maryland (Regis 1997-1998):

"This is my long-run forecast in brief: The material conditions of life will continue to get better for most people, in most countries, most of the time, indefinitely. Within a century or two, all nations and most of humanity will be at or above today's Western living standards.

"I also speculate, however, that many people *will continue to think and say* that the conditions of life are getting worse."

environmental fears were wrong and that the world was actually improving. To Lomborg's surprise, he found that Simon was mostly right. Lomborg's text is crisp, calm, clean, devastating to established dogma. Since publication, the author has been subjected to relentless *ad hominem* attacks, which can only mean his conclusions are unobjectionable in any serious scientific way.

Throughout the long controversy, Lomborg has behaved in exemplary fashion. Sadly, his critics have not. Special mention must go to the *Scientific American*, which was particularly reprehensible. All in all, the treatment accorded Lomborg can be viewed as a confirmation of the postmodern critique of science as just another power struggle. A sad episode for science.

State of Fear, p.597 (bibliography)

The Stern Review

Nicholas Stern is a Civil Service economist who drew up his review at the request of the British Government on the economic effects of global warming and possible economic cures to these ills. It was presented as a cost/benefit analyses of the 'crisis'. He assumed from the apocalyptic vision produced by the IPCC that this would lead to millions of people displaced, the poor made poorer and so forth. He claimed that the risks from unchecked climate change would be 5% of global GDP—similar to effects of a world war—but by paying now for Kyoto-type 'solutions' it would cost us just 1% of GDP.

But his review rides on the belief that the IPCC reports are correct in the horrors they predict—which, as we have seen, they are not. Unreported in the media, however, is the raft of serious academic papers which have torn his review to shreds. The main criticisms (which effectively blow it out of the water) are:

1. That he assumes the worst scenario possible.
2. The damages resulting from this misplaced assumption are themselves grossly exaggerated.
3. The cost of curing these *imaginary* problems are themselves vastly underestimated.
4. He takes no account whatever of the adaptability of human beings to changing situations. An adaptability which has enabled humans to live anywhere from the Arctic to the Equator.

It emerged that the British Government had approached other economists to author this review, making it clear that they already had assumed outcomes in mind. These economists refused to go along with this. Stern (now Lord Stern) was the first to agree to the conditions.*

* The Climatic Research Unit at University of East Anglia constructs the global temperature series that has become the *de facto* standard for the IPCC. When a researcher asked for access to examine its underlying data and methods, Professor Phil Jones, director of CRU, said: "Why should I make the data available to you, when your aim is to try and find something wrong with it?"

Given that this data set constitutes a crucial part of the background for potentially costly climate policy, we should certainly hope some researchers would spend a lot of time scrutinizing it for errors.

Unfortunately, such incidences of rejection of scrutiny are not uncommon.

Cool It, Bjørn Lomborg, page 198

As a consequence of environmentalism, not least its pressure over climate change, we are seeing incredibly expensive and highly dangerous policies based on discredited ideas being enacted which will have appalling consequences for the world's poorest peoples. One thinks of the terrible consequences of Lysenko's 'science' in the old USSR, where similarly a discredited science, amplified by a not wholly dissimilar hardened ideology, led to the starvation and death of millions.

Carbon credits and carbon trading

The iniquitous concept of carbon credits could not be better designed to cripple the Third World. There is no moral difference between buying up their carbon credits (meaning they can't build a power station but we can) and buying their organs for transplants, except that at least the organs save lives, whereas carbon credits serve no purpose but to enrich the middlemen.

Letter by the author published in the *Daily Telegraph*, Oct. 2008

Affordable and reliable energy is what helps bring people out of subsistence living and enables them to have access to clean water, safe cooking and heating, education, effective crop management, health care, communications and good transport. The only reliable source of energy available today is fossil fuel—of which there is no shortage. So why are those, who would appear to be concerned for the underdeveloped nations, so set on denying them the very resource that would get them on their feet—just because they believe in the discredited dogma of man-made global warming?

The Precautionary Principle or how to kill with kindness

A principle is defined as a fundamental truth or basis for logical argument. But precaution can never be that. It is obvious that there are times when we take precautions and times when we have to take risks. We have lots of simplistic sayings which illustrate this: "Better safe than sorry", or "nothing ventured, nothing gained" or, as Hilaire Belloc concluded his rhyme about poor young Jim in *Cautionary Tales*:
And always keep a-hold of nurse,
For fear of finding something worse.

To be honest, these trite sayings have far more wisdom than the 'Precautionary Principle', which is not a principle but an irrational taboo.

But the eco-warriors have somehow managed to turn it into a weapon against all forms of development and experimentation, particularly in technology. The results, well intended to be sure, are lethal.

Because it has no basis in reason there is no one definition of the 'principle'. But it is best summed up by the statement that nothing new must be done unless it can be shown to be 100% safe. Well, that quite effectively rules out anything and everything.

It is used *against* GM crops, *against* increasing air travel, *against* pesticides, *against* new drug treatments, *against* even using fossil fuels, *against* nuclear power, *against* encouraging industrial development in Third World countries, particularly electricity, *against* free trade, against anything in fact that is disapproved of by the back-to-nature activists. And it is always *against* something which might often save or improve lives. No-one ever seems to ask the question, "What are the risks of *not* using this technology?" to which the answer is frequently: illness, misery, starvation and death.

This is why Patrick Moore,* co-founder of Greenpeace, said, "The Environmental Movement has evolved into the strongest force there is for *preventing* development in the developing countries."†

* not the astronomer, Sir Patrick Moore.
† interview in *The Great Global Warming Swindle*, Channel 4, March 2007.

As Paul Driessen put it, in *Eco-Imperialism: Green Power, Black Death:*

At best, their blind adherence to current CSR *[Corporate Social Responsibility]* doctrine puts the European Union, United Nations, many journalists and World Business Council for Sustainable Development members like BP and Shell in league with some of the most radical elements of Western society. At worst, it makes them guilty of silent complicity (or even active collaboration) in the misery and death of millions.

The need for reform is clear. Responsible companies and politicians must demonstrate real leadership, reexamine the tenets of corporate social responsibility, and alter their stance on this radical doctrine. They must show that they truly care about people—and not just about profiting from policies sanctioned by CSR doctrines, or burnishing their reputations among Euro, green, Hollywood and media elites.

They need to lead the way in making the world a better place for its poorest inhabitants, by challenging radical ideologues on their anti-poor policies. They need to insist that doctrines of corporate social responsibility, sustainable economic development, caution and ethical investing reflect the needs of people, especially the poorest citizens of our planet. As C. S. Lewis observed:

"Of all tyrannies, a tyranny exercised for the good of its victims may be the most oppressive. It may be better to live under robber barons than under omnipotent moral busybodies. The robber baron's cruelty may sometimes sleep, his cupidity may at some point be satiated; but those who torment us for our own good will torment us without end, for they do so with the approval of their own conscience."*

* C. S. Lewis, "The Humanitarian Theory of Punishment," in *God in the Dock: Essays on Theology and Ethics*, by C. S. Lewis, edited by Walter Hooper.

The European Union

The European Union clearly goes along with the population reduction aims of activist groups. EU policies would seem to be purpose-built to prevent developing countries develop through free trade. The EU dumps its surplus food on Third World countries destroying the indigenous farmers' livelihoods and preventing imports from them by using high tariff barriers and protectionist 'regulations'. Its much vaunted 'aid' seldom gets beyond the Commissioners' or their minions' bank accounts.

As a result of the wholesale destruction of fish stocks in European (actually mostly British) waters, the EU has bought out the fishing rights from many African countries, often, by so doing, propping up iniquitous regimes and preventing their nationals from fishing in their own waters.

So why all the lies?

Paul wrote to Christians in Thessalonica:

8 And then the lawless one will be revealed, whom the Lord Jesus will overthrow with the breath of his mouth and destroy by the splendour of his coming.

9 The coming of the lawless one will be in accordance with the work of Satan displayed in all kinds of counterfeit miracles, signs and wonders,

10 and in every sort of evil that deceives those who are perishing. They perish because they refused to love the truth and so be saved.

*11 For this reason God sends them a powerful delusion **so that they will believe the lie***

12 and so that all will be condemned who have not believed the truth but have delighted in wickedness.

2 Thess 2:8-12

Strong stuff, but truth can be strong meat.

I said that behind the variety of scares we are facing lies the deepest fear of all generated by atheism. "We are here by chance, we can destroy ourselves by chance." That is the deep fear generated by atheism today.

As G. K. Chesterton observed,

"When people stop believing in God, it is not that they believe in nothing, but that they will believe in anything."

The apostle Paul expresses this in even stronger terms,

They perish because they refused to love the truth and so be saved. For this reason God sends them a powerful delusion so that they will believe the lie...

This is what we are seeing today. Because they are not prepared to look at the truth of Jesus Christ, people are being deceived by falsehoods. Yet even the science they claim to believe in is telling them that they are accepting lies. When concern for the environment got out of control decades ago now, it rapidly assumed the status of religion. But it is a false one, perhaps *the* false one.

"By their fruits you will know them" and what do we see? We see abortion, we see population control, we see children sacrificed 'for the environment', we see the poor pushed even further to the margins, while those who claim to help them mouthing platitudes but practising what is effectively genocide.

When Christianity... was shattered..., it is not merely the vices that are let loose. The vices are, indeed, let loose, and they wander and do damage. But the virtues are let loose also; and the virtues wander more wildly, and the virtues do more terrible damage. The modern world is full of the old Christian virtues gone mad. The virtues have gone mad because they have been isolated from each other and are wandering alone. Thus some scientists care for truth; and their truth is pitiless. Thus some humanitarians only care for pity; and their pity (I am sorry to say) is often untruthful.

Orthodoxy, G .K. Chesterton

As George MacDonald wrote:

"He who would do his neighbour good must first learn how not to do him harm."

If, however, we put our trust in what God tells us to do, then by loving God we can truly love our neighbour effectively.

But harm is precisely what we see happening today, caused by people with supposedly good intentions. Many activists *mean* well, but none know how to *do* well because they are believing a lie. This exchange between Bertie Wooster and 'Catsmeat' Potter-Pirbright's sister, Corky, concerning an attempt to head off the dreaded Madeleine Bassett, humorously illustrates the point,

'In the light of what you tell me.... it's a pity Catsmeat didn't hit on some other method of heading her off. I do feel that.'
My heart stood still...
'The great thing to remember, the thing to bear in mind and keep the attention fixed on, is that he meant well.'
My heart stood stiller. In your walks about London you will sometimes see bent, haggard figures that look as if they had been recently caught in some powerful machinery. They are those of fellows who got mixed up with Catsmeat when he was meaning well.
The Mating Season, P. G. Wodehouse

But behind the well-meaning but rather foolish people lie others who are by no means well-meaning. Paul speaks of "the coming of the Lawless One". Some people are always looking for naked power and control over other people. The last century has not been short of particular examples and this century looks like being no different.

We see the world's leaders jockeying for power and also aiming to bring about world governance. To do this requires draconian international laws to intimidate and control individuals and nations.

As the aim is for international rather than national control, "the environment" was soon realised to be where these controls could be put in place. The environment transcends national boundaries. Examples of how this is being done are legion—our lives are being boxed in by environmental controls, 'health and safety' controls, 'carbon footprints' etc. Engendering fear through the media has been remarkably successful—in the UK the BBC, most newspapers and television have been completely taken over by the extremist agendas. The process has begun to set up an international court to bring prosecutions over failing to prevent Climate Change.

As with all tyrannies, such as the European Union, the power seekers ensure that there are plenty of what Lenin called *poleznye idioty*—useful idiots—in the media and elsewhere. People like George Monbiot, the educational establishment, many bishops of the Church of England (there are honorable exceptions), the Roman Catholic hierarchy and other religious leaders, are so enamoured of the mythology of climate change that they do most of the indoctrination without coercion for those with the desire for power.

But step out of line and you are branded a heretic, a 'climate change' denier: a crime on a par with Holocaust denial.* Indeed it has been proposed that climate change denial should be a prosecutable offence—as we have seen, efforts are being made to bring such measures in at an international level.

---

* The semantic similarity to Holocaust deniers is often explicit and certainly represents a strong symbolic undercurrent. One Australian columnist has proposed outlawing climate change denial: "David Irving is under arrest in Austria for Holocaust Denial. Perhaps there is a case for making climate change denial an offence—it is a crime against humanity after all."

...Likewise David Roberts from *Grist* (he did their long interview with Al Gore) talks about the "denial industry" and states that we should have "war crimes trials for these bastards—some sort of climate Nuremberg."

...The UK environment minister, David Miliband, combines ridicule with declaring the debate to be over: "People say there should be a debate about global warming. But I tell you the debate is over; the reckoning has begun. The truth is staring us in the face. Climate change is here, in our country; it is an issue for our generation as well as future generations; and those who deny it are the flat-earthers of the 21st century."

Cool It, Bjørn Lomborg, pp.202-203

Too many honest scientists, having spoken up for the truth, are faced with ostracism, personal abuse and even death threats. In the past 'heretics' were burned alive: perhaps other methods of elimination will be dreamed up by the modern-day persecutors as, of course, burning people alive would be very bad for society's 'carbon footprint'.

Chapter 13

The Cosmic Ray Hypothesis

Cosmic rays were first discovered by Victor Hess in 1910. He took an electroscope (a simple device to measure static electric charge) up in a balloon. On the ground a charged electroscope gradually lost its charge, it was thought, because of natural radioactivity from rocks at ground level. But as Hess went up in his balloon he found that this discharging *increased* with height.

Hess's Electroscope experiment

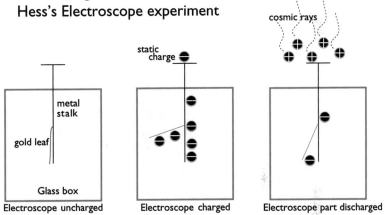

Electroscope uncharged   Electroscope charged   Electroscope part discharged

As mentioned earlier, the word 'ray' is misleading. They are in fact charged fragments of atoms smashed in the course of a supernova explosion and accelerated to speeds approaching that of the speed of light.*

* The Large Hadron Collider at CERN is able to produce similar particle speeds (see page 202). The Press hype that the LHC could produce mini black holes was quite absurd: just such high energy collisions are going on in the atmosphere all the time.

Supernovas occur when massive blue stars explode at the end of their relatively short lives (around a few hundred million years). The brilliance of such explosions within our galaxy is enormous, lasting for a few weeks. Very occasionally they can be visible to the naked eye on earth. The last such event, recorded by the Chinese, was in 1054AD. It was visible in daylight and was brighter than Venus. The star was ten times the mass of the sun and some 6300 light years away (therefore it actually exploded nearly 7300 years ago). This brief explosion was 400 billion times brighter than our sun and was the death throes of the star. Nothing remains now but an expanding cloud of dust and incandescent gas. The fragments of this explosion are accelerated to incredible speeds and the remnants of such events can be seen with telescopes as highly luminous gas clouds expanding in space (see below). They leave behind something called a neutron star—a lump of collapsed matter (electrons and protons have collapsed into one another to form an extremely dense piece of matter made of neutrons). New neutron stars spin very fast, emitting a flashing radio signal like the beam of a lighthouse and are often called pulsars for this reason.

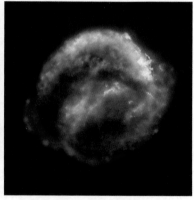

A supernova
in a neighbouring galaxy

Supernova remnants
dispersing

The resultant cosmic rays then embark on an amazing journey through our Galaxy (Milky Way), following the invisible paths created by the magnetic and gravitational fields of the billions of stars in it.

They pass through our solar system all the time like a continuous drizzle: several high energy cosmic ray particles have passed through you as you read this sentence! But before they passed through you the

CHAPTER 13

cosmic rays had to negotiate three hurdles. In the open space of the Galaxy they speed unhindered except for effects of gravity and magnetic fields. Very occasionally they might collide with the odd atom. But as they approach our solar system (or any other star system) they encounter what is called the solar wind: a stream of gas, charged particles and even plasma from the sun that streams out beyond the edge of our solar system.

Until about sixty years ago it was assumed that what wind there might be through the solar system would be toward the sun—atoms and dust particles from interstellar space being drawn toward the sun by gravity. Space is not empty but averages about one atom per cubic centimetre. But it was pointed out that comets' gaseous tails always streamed *away* from the sun as they approached in their eccentric orbits. This led to the proposition of an outward streaming solar wind which was confirmed by satellites in the following decades. This wind 'blows away' a proportion of the cosmic particles, but nonetheless many continue on their journey toward the earth where, as they approach our planet, they encounter another 'shield', this time in the form of the earth's magnetic field which surrounds our planet and which further filters the incoming cosmic radiation, particularly the relatively low energy particles.

Those that survive this then penetrate the earth's atmosphere where things get mighty complicated! They smash into atoms in the atmosphere creating a shower of secondary particles and in some cases changing one element into another. For example, cosmic rays colliding with a nitrogen atom eject a proton in the nucleus replacing it with a neutron, changing it from nitrogen (which has seven protons and seven neutrons) into carbon-14 (which has six protons and eight neutrons), also called 'radiocarbon'. ^{14}C is radioactive with a half-life of about 6000 years and decays back into nitrogen, ejecting an electron. When this form of carbon is created in the air it is absorbed by living things, both plants and animals. When they die, their remains stop taking in radiocarbon. The radiocarbon present in these remnants decays into nitrogen according to straightforward laws of physics. By measuring how much radiocarbon is found in a wooden object or other organic remains it is possible to estimate the date at which it died. This is called radiocarbon dating. Recent Creationists tend to dismiss radiocarbon dating, claiming that it has been shown to be very unreliable. We shall see why this view is mistaken.

The highest energy cosmic rays make it right through the atmosphere producing showers of *muons* (heavy electrons) at low levels. They pass through you and me even as you read this.

Danish Doubters

Now let us take up the story of a small group of Danish physicists and solar-terrestrial scientists who, in the 1980s, were uncertain about the CO_2 greenhouse hypothesis causing global warming. They preferred the likelihood that the sun was the chief agent of climate variability. But when they suggested, in their role as official delegates to the IPCC from Denmark, that one of the important areas of research that the IPCC should encourage should be solar effects on climate, the idea was dismissed almost out of hand. Right from the start this demonstrated that the IPCC worked to a specific unscientific agenda: they were already assuming that human emissions *were* the cause of climate change without any evidence.

Their names were Knud Lassen, Eigil Friis-Christensen and Henrik Svensmark. They were later joined by Nigel Marsh. Denmark is a small country but with a remarkable record of world class scientists, such as Hans Christian Ørsted, who discovered electromagnetism, and Niels Bohr, who is the father of Quantum Theory. It was therefore surprising that the IPCC should treat their suggestion in such a cavalier manner. Lassen and Friis-Christensen were already scientists of international reputation working at the Danish Meteorological Institute in Copenhagen. They were world authorities on the causes and effects of auroras. Friis-Christensen would soon take up responsibility for the preparation and launch of his Ørsted Satellite (named in honour of Hans Ørsted) as head of the Danish Space Research Institute (later renamed Danish National Space Centre), drawing together an international team of sixty scientists. This is important as it demonstrates their international reputation.

Space probes were providing more and more information about our nearest star—the sun. They showed that our sun is a variable star. Its intensity fluctuates by an average of 0.1% during a sunspot cycle of around eleven years, but also flickers rapidly at a much higher frequency (like a fluorescent light bulb). The sun also has a 'hum': this consists of sound waves travelling through the body of the sun, like earthquake tremors on the earth, only these seemed to resonate on a regular set of frequencies.

Information was being gathered about solar flares, mass ejections and their connection with sunspots, magnetic storms and auroras observed on earth. There was a very clear connection between the intensity of cosmic radiation reaching the earth and the state of the sun. Between high and low intensities the cosmic radiation fluctuated by around 20%, dropping even more during violent solar flare events.

Lassen and Friis-Christensen were interested in the connection between the sun's behaviour and variations in the climate. Others had noted that the sun's variations did seem to be reflected in the weather patterns, but the 0.1% variation was, on its own, insufficient to be the direct cause. If the sun was involved then there must be more significant factors than just light output. Lassen and Friis-Christensen had a hunch that there was. They looked afresh at the variations in cosmic rays and the variation in the sun during a series of sunspot cycles. What they noted was that there seemed to be a very good correlation between the *length* of a sunspot cycle and the fluctuations in cosmic radiation: the shorter the cycle (they could vary between 9-17 years in length—though 11 years was the average) the less cosmic radiation arrived at the earth. They were able to trace this effect back quite a long way in time from two different sets of data.

First, the record of sunspots had been kept from almost the first moment Galileo turned his telescope to the heavens.

Second, the past record of cosmic radiation is locked to the carbon-14 (^{14}C) present in organic material. Cosmic rays are the cause of the production of ^{14}C. As the sun fluctuates its solar wind, so the cosmic radiation fluctuates in the opposite direction, creating more or less ^{14}C, depending on whether the sun is weak or strong.

When carbon-14 dating was first used (in the early 1950s), the sun's fluctuations were unknown and it was assumed that ^{14}C creation over the centuries was constant. It was not long before this mistaken assumption led to some interesting historical problems. For example, ^{14}C dating put Pharaoh Zoser later than one of his successors, Pharaoh Snefru. This made no sense. But the discovery of the variation of cosmic radiation led to investigation of tree rings of ancient trees like the bristlecone pine and the bog oaks of Ireland. This showed, quite independently, the variations of ^{14}C content over several millennia.

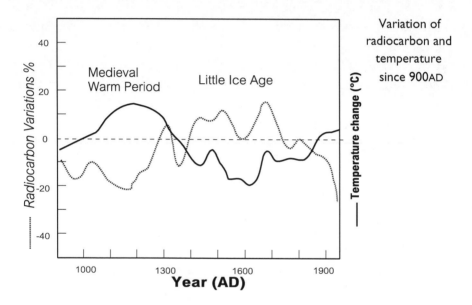

When this was fed into the ^{14}C dating scheme things began to make sense again. In passing, it was this initial mistake that led to the belief among recent creationists that ^{14}C dating 'was quite unreliable'. If they had taken the trouble to follow it through, they would see that they had missed a most interesting story.

Using this data it was shown how very clearly the cosmic ray fluctuations matched the well established temperature fluctuations of the last 1000 years.

The sunspot cycle results Lassen and Friis-Christensen published in a paper in *Science* in 1991. They drew no conclusions in the paper as to how these two things were connected. The IPCC under John Houghton dismissed these results as of no importance compared to the imminent threat of 'Global Warming' caused by human emissions of CO_2.

Because of other commitments, such as the Ørsted satellite (and Lassen's retirement), Friis-Christensen could not give full attention to these results. He was joined, however, by another physicist with an interest in climate called Henrik Svensmark. He, with encouragement from Friis-Christensen, was working on an idea about the connection between clouds, cosmic rays and cooling.

It is perhaps surprising that even in the early 1990s meteorologists had very little knowledge about the behaviour of clouds: whether they produce a net warming or cooling of the earth and how they begin to form. The super-computer models merely guessed about how they worked in the complex climate machine. These models were now drawing very pretty pictures of how climate *might* behave, but were lamentably failing to produce any accurate forecasts—long-range weather forecasting, begun in the 70s, had in effect been abandoned.

The matter of whether they cooled or warmed the planet was in fact settled in 1995 from data collected from a variety of sources. Low level clouds (as opposed to high-level cirrus) were net coolers of the earth. It is important to understand that though water *vapour* is an

---

* To be precise, a gas is a vapour above its Critical Temperature—that is, the temperature above which it is impossible to condense the gas into liquid by pressure alone. Thus, in the atmosphere oxygen (CT -118°C) and nitrogen (CT -146°C) are gases, but water vapour (CT 374°C) and carbon dioxide (CT 31.1°C) are vapours, not gases.

---

invisible greenhouse *gas,** clouds are made up of water *droplets* (or sometimes ice crystals) condensed from water vapour and have different properties. The net energy balance sheet is complicated. For example, at night, low-level cloud cover tends to act like a blanket and keep ground temperatures relatively warm: thus, in winter cloudy nights tend to be less frosty than clear nights. But equally, in the day time, the tops of these clouds reflect away more than 30% of the sun's energy. If you've ever travelled in a plane you will probably have looked down on a huge expanse of these bright white cloud tops. This, incidentally, completely upset all the computer climate models.

Svensmark, armed with this knowledge about the net cooling effect of cloud cover, pursued a possible link between cosmic rays and clouds. He began a very laborious analysis of the earth's cloud cover over the last 30 years (when satellite data of the clouds was available) and its relationship to the cosmic ray intensity. After much research he was convinced, as were others, that there was a good correlation between the two. What is more, he began to form a theory as to how these were connected.

Nearly a century earlier a Scottish physicist called Charles Wilson had produced a device called a Cloud Chamber. If clean air and water vapour are contained in a clean glass vessel connected to a piston and the piston is used to suddenly reduce the pressure, then although the water vapour should condense into water droplets it does not do so: the air is described as supersaturated with water vapour. If, however, the container is placed near a source of radioactive material then vapour trails are observed inside the glass container as the speeding particles from the radioactive source cause vapour to condense around the particles. This device became indispensable to nuclear scientists studying nuclear reactions.

In simple terms Svensmark's idea was that cosmic rays (which are just such nuclear particles) might do the same in the atmosphere by seeding the process of water vapour condensing into droplets. Of course, other particles are involved: dust, aerosols, etc. You may have seen mist developing around the smoke from a bonfire in Autumn. However, at any time the atmosphere contains supersaturated water vapour ready to be triggered into becoming a cloud.

As was seen earlier the Little Ice Age coincided with the Maunder Minimum when the sun had no sunspots. A survey of landscape paintings of the period has brought to light a very interesting detail: nearly all the paintings showed considerable cloud cover, both in winter scenes and those of summer. The three Brueghel (Pieter the Elder) paintings shown illustrate this well. The two winter scenes have slate

198

Pieter Brueghel
the elder

Left:
The Harvesters

Below:
The Bird Trap

Right:
*The Hunters in
the Snow*

grey skies and the harvest scene has only hazy sunshine. A very noticeable feature of his style is the general lack of sharp shadows. The figures, very realistic and lively, look slightly strange to us because of this lack of shadowing. Artists of the period did not see many shadows and so did not paint them.

After thorough evaluation by Svensmark and Friis-Christensen, they decided to make a press release of the discovery at the international COSPAR96 [Committee On Space Research] conference held in Birmingham in July coincident, as it happened, with the IPCC meeting that year in Geneva. Most eyes were on the political posturing going on in Geneva, where activists were pressuring the US to make huge cuts to its 'carbon emissions' as well as insisting the big Asian developing nations cut back on their use of fossil fuels in their burgeoning economies. Some small developing countries had fallen in with the activists, hoping that they could extract compensation from the rich West for causing rising sea levels. Ironically, a law suit filed by the island of Tuvalu was to fail because it was shown that sea levels had *fallen* round their islands over the last thirty years: the main cause of their flooding was the extraction by the islanders of huge amounts of sand from their beaches to build houses—they were literally digging the ground out from under their feet!*

* Michael Crichton (1942-2008), in his novel *State of Fear*, uses this real-life law suit in a thinly disguised form, calling the island 'Vanutu'. The novel is unusual in that its prime purpose is didactic on the issue of climate change. His research was very thorough.

At Geneva the fearmongering by politicians and activists, flinging rational science to the winds, went on apace; in Birmingham Svensmark's research results were released. The press took only a little interest: *The Times* reported the discovery in a somewhat sceptical manner. The BBC led with the news of the US falling into line in Geneva, then a brief account of Svensmark's work was reported on by their then science correspondent, David Whitehouse: he reported that the discovery might "undermine our thinking about global warming",[†] the first and probably the last piece of honest reporting by a BBC reporter on the topic. Whitehouse was later to leave the BBC and remains sceptical of the greenhouse hypothesis. The BBC no longer has any qualified scientist on their reporting staff. He was their last.

When Bolin heard about the discovery he was scathing. He declared, "I find the move from this pair scientifically extremely naive and irresponsible."†

Ben Santer, one of the major players at the top of the IPCC, said, "I am particularly sceptical about scientists who believe they have a hotline to God."†

As the discovery included the new data about the cooling effect of clouds, the IPCC were facing a double whammy: their computer models were completely wrong and there was now a rival to the greenhouse hypothesis.

To be fair to Bolin, he later changed his mind about their work. "It is pleasing to see such a sane and sincere scientific investigation, ... It differs quite a lot from other questionings of the greenhouse effect. Naturally I was surprised by the big changes they report, in the clouds ... I can't see that their findings are given a satisfactory explanation. They do not conclude anything about the effects of human activity. But there is no doubt that this is serious science."†

Bolin was shortly to retire from the IPCC, but he clearly realised that the discoveries had put a huge question mark over the whole greenhouse hypothesis. But the greenhouse idea was now a runaway horse; huge amounts of political and real capital and huge numbers of jobs were now tied up in it. To admit doubt, let alone declare it mistaken, was increasingly not an option any more. Tens of thousands of jobs now depended on treating the fantasy as a fact.

† Quoted in *The Manic Sun*, Nigel Calder, pp.179-180

CERN, *European Organisation for Nuclear Research*.
Inset: part of the Large Hadron Collider.

Here the CLOUD (see page 205) experiment was finally
conducted in 2011.
The results are best summarised on:
http://calderup.wordpress.com/

Chapter 14

A Setback

During the 1990s Svensmark continued to build evidence for natural warmings and coolings being related to cosmic radiation counts from all around the globe. One example was from the records kept for centuries in China about dates of the arrival of Spring at the Yangtze River. When these were compared to the sunspot cycle lengths (remember, short sunspot cycles mean low cosmic radiation levels) the following graph of correlation could be plotted.

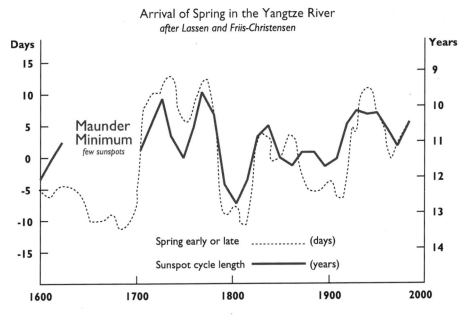

Arrival of Spring in the Yangtze River
after Lassen and Friis-Christensen

It all seemed to be coming together, but then came a serious setback.

It has been known since the early 20th century that the earth reverses its magnetic field—this occurs at irregular intervals of the order of 700-900 thousand years. Sometimes the earth attempts a magnetic reversal which fails. An example of one such event left evidence in the rocks at Laschamp in France about 40,000 years ago.

During these reversals or near reversals the magnetic field intensity drops toward zero over a period of a few thousand years (there is some evidence to suggest we may be heading that way again soon). This would affect the shielding the earth has against cosmic and solar radiation and therefore if the cosmic ray/cloud hypothesis is correct one might expect coolings to occur during these periods. A team led by Jürg Beer of the Swiss Institute of Environmental Science and Technology investigated the event at Laschamp and found that there seemed to be no noticeable change in the temperature during that period. Here was genuine scientific research which cast very proper scientific doubt on Svensmark's idea.

When a scientist has a hypothesis that has scientific objections based on observations then he can do one of two things: abandon the hypothesis or modify the hypothesis.

Naturally any scientist will look at the second option as well as the first one if he already seems to have a considerable amount of supporting data.

As it happened, Svensmark had already got a suspicion as to a possible explanation for both the Laschamp Excursion (as these failed reversals are called) and the actual magnetic reversals not producing noticeable cooling. When he pursued this suspicion he discovered that it was correct.

The earth's magnetic shield is the second barrier against incoming solar and cosmic particles or rays. Of the two, cosmic rays have the wider spread of energy levels, the highest levels of which considerably exceed those from the sun—indeed, this was one of the ways of distinguishing cosmic from solar particles. However, the earth's shield was known to be far less effective against these highest energy level particles. These are the ones which penetrate deepest into the earth. The results of the impact of the high energy cosmic rays on the atmosphere are very complex, but the net result is that particles called muons of very high energy penetrate to ground level. It is these particles which are primarily responsible for the formation of the low-level clouds that cause the cooling and it is the origin of these particles that the earth's magnetic shield is the *least* effective screen—screening out less than 3% of them. Thus, when the earth's shield fails, as in a magnetic reversal or a Laschamp episode, it would make hardly any difference to the intensity of muons causing cloud formation. The solar wind on the other hand continues to 'blow away' many of these high-energy particles.

Once this important difficulty had been resolved, an excellent example of how proper scientific debate should be conducted, Svensmark turned his mind to how an experiment could be devised which would enable him to measure and observe exactly how these high-energy muons were starting cloud formation.

The best place for such experiments was at CERN—the European accelerator under Switzerland. Here particles might be accelerated to speeds equivalent to cosmic rays and their interaction with air could be carefully observed and measured. Negotiations to conduct such an experiment were begun in 1998, but were hampered by budget and by the fact that CERN was busy building the Large Hadron Collider. At one point it looked like an agreement for go ahead was given, only to have it overturned because of CERN's budget restraints. Suffice it to say that the go ahead was finally given and experiments began in 2010—the experiment being given the acronym CLOUD (Cosmics Leaving OUtdoor Droplets).*

Meanwhile, Svensmark decided that an experiment could be done using the naturally occurring cosmic rays that are whizzing through us all the time.

In 2005, in a basement at the Danish National Space Centre, Svensmark designed a large teflon-lined box into which precise mixtures of gases could be introduced which would simulate the real atmosphere. An array of measuring instruments and control equipment would enable careful observation of what the cosmic rays were doing, how much they were doing and how quickly. He called it the SKY (the Danish word for cloud) experiment.

The full details of the experiment are too complex for this book, but an account of it can be read in *The Chilling Stars* by Svensmark and

Calder. But the results were beyond what Svensmark had anticipated. The cosmic rays did indeed seed clouds and with a speed and efficiency that was quite unexpected. This was clear experimental evidence that the cosmic ray/cloud theory was on the right track.*

Three years before this, however, the theory had received another boost from a quite unexpected quarter.

* A fascinating documentary of the story of Svensmark's research, called *The Cloud Mystery*, directed by Lars Oxfieldt Mortensen, is available from *www.thecloudmystery.com* as a DVD.

Chapter 15

The Star Factor

Then God said, "Let there be lights in the expanse of the heavens to separate the day from the night, and let them be for signs, and for seasons, and for days and years; Gen 1:14

As mentioned before, the solar system moves in and out of a spiral arm of the Galaxy roughly every 140 million years. This movement through the Galaxy was worked out by the Jewish astrophysicist Nir Shaviv from the University of Jerusalem and confirmed by paleogeologist Jan Veizer through the remarkable effect this has had on very long-term climate trends on the earth (using ^{18}O in the shells of very ancient sea creatures).

When these two met to pool their results in 2002 they realised that Svensmark's theory accounted very well for the fact that, as we move into more dense areas of stars, cosmic radiation will rise considerably, meaning that the earth will be cooled by cloud formation: this would account for the Ice Ball Earth events and also some of the major ice ages which corresponded to our passing through the different arms of the galaxy.

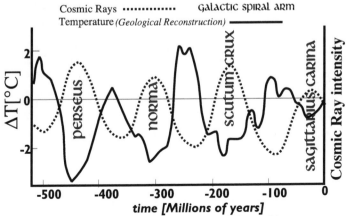

Phanerozoic Temperature related to Galactic Movement

Such a tie up was an unexpected bonus and showed, as with any good theory, that it was able to explain the unexpected. Indeed, it looks as though the data can be reversed: cold periods can be used to identify when and even where a 'local' star might have exploded, creating the cosmic rays that caused the cold period.

This tie up was the climate change issue writ large.

Our climate ultimately comes from the stars. It is out there that cosmic rays are born in supernovas and spread out through the galaxy. It is not too extreme to suggest that a supernova that exploded, say, fifty million years ago caused the storm last Thursday week!

Cosmic rays have affected climate from periods of over hundreds of millions (even billions) of years down to years, months and days, even hours and minutes!

Clouds are the ongoing key to weather. Cosmic rays are the key to the clouds, the sun is the gate-keeper for cosmic rays and the galaxy is the source of the rays. Of course, there are other major complicating factors involved in weather. Using the analogy of an orchestra, the clouds are the strings section, nearly always having a part to play. CO_2's part, on this analogy, is to be a mere member of the audience!

This brings us back to the central contention (or rather the Bible's contention) that God is in charge of the weather. One way to look at what science is discovering is to see the Galaxy (and indeed other galaxies) as vast databases and programmes for the weather on the earth. Not one star explodes without the knowledge and decision of God. Each exploded star will have a contribution (however small) to the earth's weather.

Lift your eyes and look to the heavens:
Who created all these?
He who brings out the starry host one by one,
and calls them each by name.
Because of his great power and mighty strength,
not one of them is missing.

Is 40:26

Are not two sparrows sold for a penny? Yet not one of them
will fall to the ground apart from the will of your Father.

And even the very hairs of your head are all numbered.
*So don't be afraid; you are worth more than many sparrows.**

Mt 10:29–31

* Contrary to the views held by some environmentalists, one of whom, Eric Bettelheim (executive chairman of Sustainable Forestry Management) stated that human beings are "the disease on the planet." [*intelligence²* Green Festival Conference, 25th Jan 2009, held at the Royal Geographical Society]

BLESS the LORD, O my soul!
O LORD my God, You are very great;
You are clothed with splendor and majesty,
Covering Yourself with light as with a cloak,
Stretching out heaven like a tent curtain.
He lays the beams of His upper chambers in the waters;
He makes the clouds His chariot;
He walks upon the wings of the wind;
He makes the winds His messengers,
Flaming fire His ministers.
He established the earth upon its foundations,
So that it will not totter forever and ever.

Ps 104:1–5 NASB

And of the angels He says,
"WHO MAKES HIS ANGELS WINDS,
AND HIS MINISTERS A FLAME OF FIRE."

Heb 1:7 NASB

Here the Psalmist is proclaiming God's control over the physical world; in particular its weather: it is intriguing that the ministers (the ones who carry out their Lord's commands) of this are described as 'flames of fire'; in my view, more than just a poetic coincidence: the supernovas (the flames of fire) are literally the ministers of weather by their production of cosmic rays.

As we have seen, it has been possible to chart throughout history and in prehistory when cosmic rays have been more or less intense and see its knock-on effect on global temperatures. Do they relate to specific Bible events?

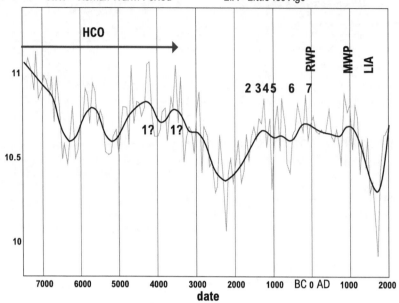

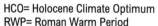

HCO= Holocene Climate Optimum   MWP= Medieval Warm Period
RWP= Roman Warm Period   LIA= Little Ice Age

A Climate Temperature Reconstruction

We might date creation of Adam and Eve somewhere around what is called the Holocene Climate Optimum, starting some ten thousand years ago. The ice was melting rapidly and the Middle East was warm and relatively moist and fertile.

Connecting events to the current understanding of climate history is very much work in progress. Still, it could help to sharpen up the dating of some of the following events (see figure above):

1. The Flood—this is a big topic and needs a separate book, but might be located somewhere around 4500-3500BC or around 2400BC, depending on whether colder or warmer meant wetter in the area of Mesopotamia: the 'cataracts of the deep' suggest not just rainfall but a huge meltwater inundation or perhaps an ocean break-through to create what is now the Black Sea.

2. The Famine in Egypt (Joseph)—cold periods tend to produce drought in Africa, with the Nile failing to flood leading to famine. As the periods were short term: seven and seven years, this was most likely to

210   CHAPTER 15

have been caused by solar variations: a sunspot cycle not taking place 'as expected' but being delayed, leading to reduced rainfall in the highlands associated with the Nile, leading to less than expected flooding. Even so, the chart suggests a cooler period.

3. The Plagues and the Exodus.

Both of these have weather-related miracles—often understood as miracles of *timing*, though mostly natural in nature. Thus Exodus:

Then Moses *stretched out his hand over the sea, and all that night the LORD drove the sea back with a strong east wind and turned it into dry land. The waters were divided, and the Israelites went through the sea on dry ground, with a wall of water on their right and on their left.*

Ex 14:21-22

It has been speculated that if we are looking at the tip of the Red Sea as the crossing place, what took place was a tsunami combined with the east wind. An undersea earthquake in the Red Sea region (a highly active tectonic plate area) would first cause the water to withdraw from the top of the Red Sea, leaving dry land. The water on either side being caused by a normally underwater natural causeway being exposed. The Israelites cross over and then the tsunami wave train comes back in, sweeping away the Egyptian pursuers.

4. As the Israelites conquered Canaan it would indeed be a land flowing with milk and honey: the rising temperature would be improving fertility and crop yields just at the time of the conquest.

5. The period of David and Solomon around 1000/900BC seems to be a medium warm period and the trend would still be towards more prosperous times.

6. The Assyrian and Babylonian period: Seems to coincide with deteriorating conditions leading to invasions as peoples looked for food when crop yields deteriorated.

All of this must be regarded as somewhat speculative. But it could be a fascinating area of Biblical study relating climate change to biblical events, just as is currently done with archaeology.

7. The Roman Warm Period: Another warm period as evidenced by, among other indicators, the spread of viticulture north into Britain and even southern Scotland by the third century AD.

8. Moving beyond the biblical period we pass through another cooler period before coming to the Medieval Warm Period.

This was when Greenland was colonised by the Vikings in around 900AD. These colonies thrived until the relatively rapid onset of the Little Ice Age around 1350. Then the settlers began to die out from cold and starvation.

A famous defeat was caused by the bad weather associated with the depths of the Little Ice Age; that of the Spanish Armada beginning the 8th August 1588.

On the medal struck to commemorate the English victory, on the obverse, is a picture of the engagement of the fleets, above, in the clouds, is the name יהוה in Hebrew. The legend reads:

+ FLAVIT + *YAHWEH* + ET + DISSIPATI + SVNT + 1588

God blew and they were scattered

The Little Ice Age only really went into reverse around the 1850s and temperatures have risen slightly since then, but have recently stalled and fallen again slightly since 1998.

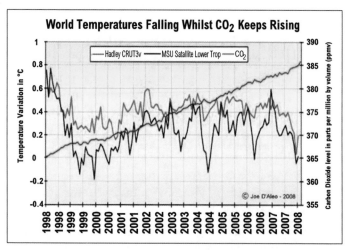

After Dr Piers Corbyn. *www.weatheraction.com*

Chapter 16

The Days of Creation

It is one of the themes of this book that the days of Genesis Ch.1 are best understood as periods of special creativity by God. But Genesis is silent about the 'how' of the successive creations of each day. "God said... and it was so." yet in all God's subsequent great acts, culminating in his great Act of Redemption through Jesus, there is process, often long drawn out process filled with the detail of individual lives touched by God down the centuries. The genealogies spell out the patient, careful preparation over thousands of years that one particular person should be born.

Like the cosmic rays setting out on their amazing journey through the Galaxy in order to reach this tiny planet and start a particular cloud formation to produce a particular rain storm with unerring aim, *He makes the winds His messengers, Flaming fire His ministers,* so these fiery messengers from the Galaxy may serve other great purposes of God.

The power of change and creativity

11 Then God said, "Let the earth sprout vegetation: plants yielding seed, and fruit trees on the earth bearing fruit after their kind with seed in them"; and it was so.

12 The earth brought forth vegetation, plants yielding seed after their kind, and trees bearing fruit with seed in them, after their kind; and God saw that it was good.

13 There was evening and there was morning, a third day.

14 Then God said, "Let there be lights in the expanse of the heavens to separate the day from the night, and let them be for signs and for seasons and for days and years;

15 and let them be for lights in the expanse of the heavens to give light on the earth"; and it was so.

16 God made the two great lights, the greater light to govern the day, and the lesser light to govern the night; He made the stars also.

17 God placed them in the expanse of the heavens to give light on the earth,

18 and to govern the day and the night, and to separate the light from the darkness; and God saw that it was good.

19 There was evening and there was morning, a fourth day.

20 Then God said, "Let the waters teem with swarms of living creatures, and let birds fly above the earth in the open expanse of the heavens."

21 God created the great sea monsters and every living creature that moves, with which the waters swarmed after their kind, and every winged bird after its kind; and God saw that it was good.

22 God blessed them, saying, "Be fruitful and multiply, and fill the waters in the seas, and let birds multiply on the earth."

23 There was evening and there was morning, a fifth day.

24 Then God said, "Let the earth bring forth living creatures after their kind: cattle and creeping things and beasts of the earth after their kind"; and it was so.

25 God made the beasts of the earth after their kind, and the cattle after their kind, and everything that creeps on the ground after its kind; and God saw that it was good.

26 Then God said, "Let Us make man in Our image, according to Our likeness; and let them rule over the fish of the sea and over the birds of the sky and over the cattle and over all the earth, and over every creeping thing that creeps on the earth."

Gen 1:11-26 NASB

Notice again the economy of style that Moses uses. God speaks, "Let...", then God "makes" or "creates" a list of creatures, "after their kind", but the text refrains for commenting on how the word spoken became the creature, how the *word* became *flesh*; how God's command is brought about in his creation.

If we look at the supreme example of the Word becoming flesh in the coming of Jesus Christ, maybe this will help us understand a bit more.

His birth was a combination of the miraculous (Mary conceives by the Holy Spirit) and the natural—when all the normal processes of gestation and birth began. The egg in Mary was also natural, but her genealogy had been prepared by God beforehand from the creation of Adam. Each step in that genealogy was natural and the whole process took thousands of years to come to that moment when Jesus, the Eternal Word, became an embryo in Mary's womb.

We suggest that the process for bringing about specific creations, following God's declaration, both took time and required a mechanism. The Bible does not specify what that might be. But we may be able to find out how it might work.

And of the angels He says,
"WHO MAKES HIS ANGELS WINDS,
AND HIS MINISTERS A FLAME OF FIRE."

God uses ministers to cause his will to be obeyed in his Creation: we have already seen how cosmic rays cause the weather patterns from day to day.

But cosmic rays do other things besides affecting the weather: they change atoms in molecules from one element to another and in some molecules this will cause them to rearrange. This is particularly true in the molecules that make up the living cell. A single change in an atom in one protein or one part of a DNA molecule can cause changes of function.

So what might this imply? Firstly, that these cosmic ray strikes are not random. God holds all creation in his hands and sustains it moment by moment, through his Son:

The Son is the radiance of God's glory and the exact representation of his being, sustaining all things by his powerful word. After he had provided purification for sins, he sat down at the right hand of the Majesty in heaven. Heb 1:3

Some of these rays (ministers of God's purposes) have a planned path to strike and alter a specific atom or series of atoms, even though they may have travelled several hundred thousand light years through the galaxy. We may find the idea of an accurate 'hit' at that range mind-boggling, but to God it is a small matter.

What I am suggesting is that these specific hits are *designed* to bring about the particular changes in genes to create new species. We know that chromosomes (the entire gene sequence of a species) contain dormant gene sequences that can be switched on. A simple signal initiated by a single cosmic ray 'strike' could easily do this. Look at it as the ultimate molecular key-hole surgery! Nothing invasive, just the simplest adjustment and the fruit is a remarkable change in the offspring of an animal. There is nothing 'random' about this process—it is not useful to use the word mutation—which suggests accident: there is nothing accidental in God's purposes.

Everyone, evolutionist and creationist, agrees that there is a remarkable resemblance in the body designs of most animals: similar skeletons, internal organs etc. The Evolutionist merely thinks of random changes, but the Creationist, with far more justification, sees Design. A true artist has a style which competent art collectors can recognise pretty quickly: how much more so is this true of God the Trinity, Creator and Redeemer? In the case of art, craft and even technology, human beings are, in a tiny way, acting in the image of God.

And how does a human artist, craftsman or engineer set about creating? Sometimes from a blank sheet of paper, but far more often by carefully building up, from initially simple ideas or components, the complex and sophisticated picture or piece of furniture or bit of technology. We must not press this too far: God doesn't 'experiment' with design—as far as we know anyway—though the passage about the potter in Jeremiah gets quite near to that possibility.

But to return to the delicate molecular surgery of the cosmic ray, it would seem that the work of the cosmic ray on DNA and its work on changing the climate from time to time go hand in hand.

Remember how Shaviv and Veizer discovered the Galactic arm traverse every 140 million years (see page 207). As the earth passed through a Galactic arm it was bathed in far higher amounts of cosmic radiation. Cosmic radiation is much stronger when we are inside a galactic arm than when we are travelling between arms. This is because there are many more stars in the vicinity and inevitably therefore more 'shrapnel' from local supernovas.

The results have been dramatic climate shifts on earth. And these climate shifts have an effect on the new animals created by DNA changes caused also by the cosmic radiation. The new animals have new genes that enable them to adapt to the changed external conditions.

Incidentally, within species there are remarkable repositories of 'spare' genes as well: genes which are in the DNA but do not seem to be activated. Someone described them as 'junk genes': they are not useless, but, like junk, are stored in the DNA's equivalent of the attic—just in case a use can be found for them one day. When conditions change—particularly climate—then these genes can be activated or others shut down and the creature becomes adapted to the new environment: human beings are an excellent example of adaptability, able to live successfully from the Arctic to the tropics.

During the period of the creation of animal life on earth (the last 550 million years or so) we have passed in and out of four arms of our galaxy—in astronomical terms, maybe Days Three to Six in Genesis. It looks very much as if the new creations came out of the times of maximum climate variations: creation events thriving on dramatic conditions. If we combine the diagrams of the geological epochs from page 49 and the traversing of the Galactic arms on page 207 we can see this idea a bit more clearly over the page. This diagram is not fact, but hypothesis based on the scientific data and on what Genesis may be suggesting.

Since the time of Adam, perhaps 7000-8000 years ago, however, we have been living in a remarkably stable period of earth's long history. Dramatic cosmic events may be the agents of God's new creations, but stable periods are times of God blessing his creation.

But we can also see from Scripture that as God prepares to bring about his New Heaven and New Earth there will once more be dramatic cosmic events. In Matthew's gospel Ch.24 Jesus not only speaks about signs in the sky:

"Immediately after the distress of those days 'the sun will be darkened, and the moon will not give its light; the stars will fall from the sky, and the heavenly bodies will be shaken.'

"At that time the sign of the Son of Man will appear in the sky, and

all the nations of the earth will mourn. They will see the Son of Man coming on the clouds of the sky, with power and great glory."

Mt 24:29-30

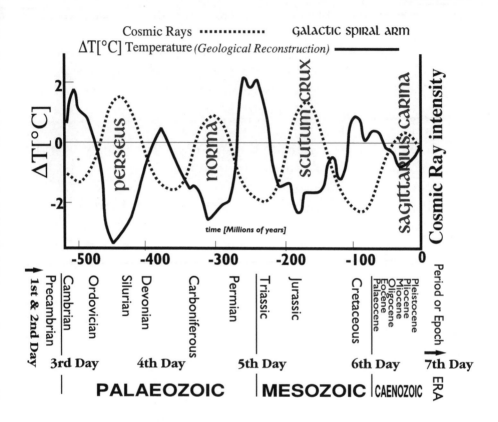

But he also speaks in terms of birth pangs. A pregnancy is a nine-month process and may seem fairly 'stable' until the dramatic time for giving birth starts:

"All these are the beginning of birth-pains."   Mt 24:8

Although we may know a good deal about the cosmos, that does not mean we can ever predict what may happen in the heavens: a supernova, for example, is not a very predictable event.

It may seem trite to put this question, but are we ready for what may come? The universe we live in is not predictable, nor is it particularly safe. It is stunningly dramatic. Despite the West's obsession with 'safety', we are still at the behest of the forces in creation quite outside our control, which means we are at the mercy of God's handiwork and of God himself. This fact should instill awe in us, but it can also instill fear, fear of our insignificance in the unimaginable vastness of the Universe. Surely the God who creates galaxies by the billion cannot have the slightest concern for the little specks of living organic matter crawling around on a tiny planet?

This, however, is a relatively modern nightmare, spawned from agnosticism and atheism (aberrations in any age). God showed the prophet Isaiah that the exact opposite is true:

25 "To whom will you compare me?
Or who is my equal?" says the Holy One.
26 Lift your eyes and look to the heavens:
Who created all these?
He who brings out the starry host one by one,
and calls them each by name.
Because of his great power and mighty strength,
not one of them is missing.
27 Why do you say, O Jacob,
and complain, O Israel,
"My way is hidden from the LORD;
my cause is disregarded by my God"?
28 Do you not know?
Have you not heard?
The LORD is the everlasting God,
the Creator of the ends of the earth.
He will not grow tired or weary,
and his understanding no-one can fathom.
29 He gives strength to the weary
and increases the power of the weak.
30 Even youths grow tired and weary,
and young men stumble and fall;
31 but those who hope in the LORD
will renew their strength.
They will soar on wings like eagles;

they will run and not grow weary,
they will walk and not be faint.

God shows Isaiah that it is just *because* he is almighty that he is able to act to redeem every individual. The God who can direct a single cosmic ray unerringly to its target is surely able to manage a human being!

Once we grasp this fact, then we can stop going our own way, frightened, fearful and, yes, sinful. Let Isaiah say it:

We all, like sheep, have gone astray,
each of us has turned to his own way;
and the LORD has laid on him
the iniquity of us all.

Is 53:6

Though human beings have, without doubt, achieved remarkable things, there is a permanent sense of lostness, *angst*, and sense of ultimate futility:

1 The words of the Teacher, son of David, king of Jerusalem:
2 "Meaningless! Meaningless!" says the Teacher.
"Utterly meaningless! Everything is meaningless."
3 What does man gain from all his labour
at which he toils under the sun?"

Eccles 1:1-3

We need the way out. If we can find eternal security it frees us from the fears that prevent us from acting now to help in the many miseries and needs of this temporary but important world. As Lomborg reminded his readers, "... mankind's lot has *vastly improved.* This does not, however, mean that everything is *good enough.* The first statement refers to what the world looks like, whereas the second refers to what it ought to look like."

All improvements are of course ultimately doomed. On any philosophy, the death of the individual would be perceived as ultimately failure of this world to improve his lot! As every doctor

220   CHAPTER 16

knows, each patient is a 'dead man walking', but that does not stop the doctor helping to heal disease and illness as far as he can. If he allows the sense of ultimate futility to overwhelm him, he will lose his capacity to help at all.

But it is the contention of the Bible that though this sense of futility is real enough it is not the ultimate truth. God offers eternal security, so that we may act in this world with compassion and love toward those who are suffering, using our intelligence to optimise our actions. Two men drowning cannot save each other, though they may offer each other support. One man with a foot firmly planted on the bank can save a drowning man. Eternal security gives us true ability to reach out to the suffering.

Remember when we looked at Genesis Ch.1, how the Bible day begins with rest and leads on to work?

God would first give us his rest: rest from our nagging consciences, our real sin and failure as well as desire to 'succeed' and get ahead.

28 "Come to me, all you who are weary and burdened, and I will give you rest.

29 Take my yoke upon you and learn from me, for I am gentle and humble in heart, and you will find rest for your souls.

30 For my yoke is easy and my burden is light."

Mt 11:28-30

But how do we receive this lifeline? It is both hard and simple. God himself, by entering our world in his Son Jesus, brings us the lifeline we desperate need. Strangely, it was by his death on a cross that sin and death were cancelled forever.

And as Peter wrote:

For Christ died for sins once for all, the righteous for the unrighteous, to bring you to God. He was put to death in the body but made alive by the Spirit,

1 Pet 3:18

As the apostle John put it:

8 If we claim to be without sin, we deceive ourselves and the truth is not in us.

9 If we confess our sins, he is faithful and just and will forgive us our sins and purify us from all unrighteousness.

1 Jn 1:8-9

As the writer of the letter to the Hebrews put it:

We have this hope as an anchor for the soul, firm and secure. It enters the inner sanctuary behind the curtain, where Jesus, who went before us, has entered on our behalf. He has become a high priest for ever, in the order of Melchizedek.

Heb 6:19-20

Once secure in the forgiveness that Christ gives to all who turn to him, we are freed from the *angst* of the age. There is work to be done in God's world, but we cannot do it by ourselves; but with his help we can go out and work for him in his world, in his universe, where all things are ultimately part of God's plan and purpose.

Then the angel showed me the river of the water of life, as clear as crystal, flowing from the throne of God and of the Lamb down the middle of the great street of the city. On each side of the river stood the tree of life, bearing twelve crops of fruit, yielding its fruit every month. And the leaves of the tree are for the healing of the nations.

No longer will there be any curse. The throne of God and of the Lamb will be in the city, and his servants will serve him.

Rev 22:1-3

Appendix 1
The Death of the Greenhouse Hypothesis (1824 - 1909)

Therefore everyone who hears these words of mine and puts them into practice is like a wise man who built his house on the rock. The rain came down, the streams rose, and the winds blew and beat against that house; yet it did not fall, because it had its foundation on the rock. But everyone who hears these words of mine and does not put them into practice is like a foolish man who built his house on sand. The rain came down, the streams rose, and the winds blew and beat against that house, and it fell with a great crash." Matthew 7:24–27

There is no doubt that the belief in man-made climate change through the impact of so-called 'greenhouse' gases - carbon dioxide [CO_2] methane [CH_4] water vapour [H_2O] ozone [O_3] and nitrous oxide [N_2O] has produced an enormous edifice which has financial, political, philosophical and even religious aspects. But is it built on rock or sand?

It is vital to understand that this huge superstructure depends entirely on the belief in the *greenhouse hypothesis*. If that is shown to be false, then everything else completely collapses.

The greenhouse hypothesis

As its name suggests this hypothesis tries to explain a well known phenomenon. The air inside a glass greenhouse can maintain a much higher temperature that the surrounding atmosphere - though this difference depends on their being a reasonable amount of direct sunlight. We have all experienced this in our cars when they have been left standing in the sun - the inside surfaces become very hot, even too hot to touch - and the air also becomes very warm indeed.

The hypothesis is a very old one. Glass, as it happens, is opaque to some radiation in the infrared [IR] part of the spectrum - the part we can call 'heat radiation'. Direct sunlight passes through the glass, losing a little of the infrared on the way in. The sun's radiation is absorbed by the ground in the greenhouse, where it is re-emitted by the ground in the lower frequencies of the infrared. The glass traps these rays and re-emits them into the greenhouse, stoking up the heat. It is sometimes referred to as a radiation trap - or so the hypothesis claims.

Two key things to note:

1. It is assumed that nearly all the sun's radiation (such as light) is turned into heat radiation at the ground - called a transformation of wavelength.
2. That the IR radiated back by the glass further warms the ground and therefore the air inside the greenhouse.

This is what physics teachers and textbooks have taught for more than a century and so it is considered an established fact.

Although the hypothesis goes back to 1824 (Fourier), hardly anyone has tested the hypothesis by doing any experiments. But a hundred years ago, one man did. Prof R.W.Wood was doubtful about the hypothesis. Here are his notes on his thoughts and his subsequent experiment.

Note on the Theory of the Greenhouse
by Professor R. W. Wood, 1909.

There appears to be a widespread belief that the comparatively high temperature produced within a closed space covered with glass, and exposed to solar radiation, results from a transformation of wave-length, that is, that the heat waves from the sun, which are able to penetrate the glass, fall upon the walls of the enclosure and raise its temperature: the heat energy is re-emitted by the walls in the form of much longer waves, which are unable to penetrate the glass, the greenhouse acting as a radiation trap.

I have always felt some doubt as to whether this action played any very large part in the elevation of temperature. It appeared much more probable that the part played by the glass was the prevention of the escape of the warm air heated by the ground within the enclosure. If we open the doors of a greenhouse on a cold and windy day, the trapping of radiation appears to lose much of its efficacy. As a matter of fact I am of the opinion that a greenhouse made of a glass transparent to waves of every possible length would show a temperature nearly, if not quite, as high as that observed in a glass house. The transparent screen allows the solar radiation to warm the ground, and the ground in turn warms the air, but only the limited amount within the enclosure. In the "open," the ground is continually brought into contact with cold air by convection currents.

224

To test the matter I constructed two enclosures of dead black cardboard, one covered with a glass plate, the other with a plate of rock-salt of equal thickness. The bulb of a thermometer was inserted in each enclosure and the whole packed in cotton, with the exception of the transparent plates which were exposed. When exposed to sunlight the temperature rose gradually to 65°C, the enclosure covered with the salt plate keeping a little ahead of the other, owing to the fact that it transmitted the longer waves from the sun, which were stopped by the glass. In order to eliminate this action the sunlight was first passed through a glass plate.

There was now scarcely a difference of one degree between the temperatures of the two enclosures. The maximum temperature reached was about 55°C. From what we know about the distribution of energy in the spectrum of the radiation emitted by a body at 55°C, it is clear that the rock-salt plate is capable of transmitting practically all of it, while the glass plate stops it entirely. This shows us that the loss of temperature of the ground by radiation is very small in comparison to the loss by convection, in other words that we gain very little from the circumstance that the radiation is trapped.

Is it therefore necessary to pay attention to trapped radiation in deducing the temperature of a planet as affected by its atmosphere? The solar rays penetrate the atmosphere, warm the ground which in turn warms the atmosphere by contact and by convection currents. The heat received is thus stored up in the atmosphere, remaining there on account of the very low radiating power of a gas. It seems to me very doubtful if the atmosphere is warmed to any great extent by absorbing the radiation from the ground, even under the most favourable conditions.

This extremely simple and elegant experiment could be easily replicated in any school science class with equally simple equipment. The experiment was successfully repeated in 2011 by Prof. Nasif Nahle:*

Wood's results are a falsification of the greenhouse hypothesis. Glass (with its IR absorbing properties) clearly does not act as a radiation trap, being less effective than the rock salt crystal plate at warming the covered space.

The idea that the glass, absorbing then re-radiating IR, further warms the greenhouse, cannot be correct anyway as it would break the laws of thermodynamics: "heat cannot of itself pass from a cooler body to a hotter body". The glass is *cooler* than the ground inside the greenhouse. If you need confirmation of this fact, try a simple test next time you go to your car after parking it in the sun. First feel the temperature of the dashboard, then feel the temperature of the windscreen. The windscreen will be cool by comparison. If you have a thermometer of the colour sensitive variety, test each surface with that and you will find this to be true.

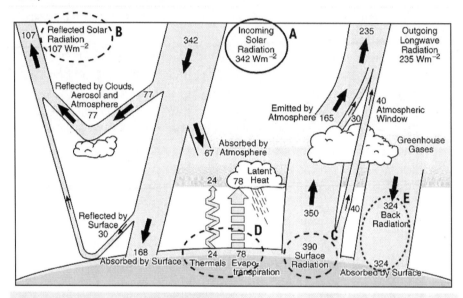

This is the official IPCC diagram explaining the greenhouse hypothesis whereby gases such as carbon dioxide and methane supposedly warm up the planet. It was put together by Kiehl & Trenberth who are members of the coterie of scientists at the heart of the IPCC.

It shows the rate of input of energy from the Sun at 342 Wm[-2] (watt per square meter) **A** of which 107 is reflected **B** and 235 is absorbed by the atmosphere or the ground, yet, amazingly, the diagram shows the ground radiating back 390 Wm[-2] **C** plus 24 + 78 **D** = a whopping **492** Wm[-2].

This is more than a 40% increase in the total amount of energy originally received from the Sun! Where has this miraculous supply of energy appeared from? From nowhere: the strange flows of energy in the right hand part of the diagram (in particular **E**) is an illusion - what they appear to have done is to count energy twice and enable that energy to flow 'uphill': they make a *cooler* atmosphere somehow heat a *warmer* earth's surface. If this could really happen then we need never burn any more coal or gas or nuclear fuel because we could supply ourselves with infinite energy using just the tiniest radiant source and a mirror.

The air is always cooler than the ground below it - see the graph. ➔ So it is of no significance whatever that CO_2 etc happen to absorb certain IR frequencies - the only conceivable effect that might have is a (very tiny) reduction in the surface temperature and hence the temperature of the atmosphere.

So the second premise of the hypothesis is falsified by this experiment.

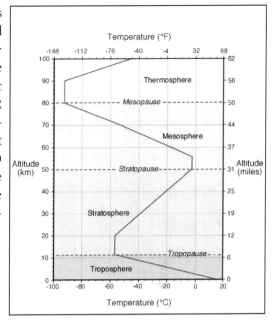

Therefore the greenhouse hypothesis is proved wrong both by experiment and by the fact that, if correct, it would violate the laws of thermodynamics and enable unlimited energy to be extracted from any radiation source. These fundamental errors at the root of the whole greenhouse hypothesis means that its foundation is built on 'sand' not 'rock'.

The Moon paradox

One of the staple arguments for a general greenhouse effect on earth is the assertion that this planet would be an overall 30-35K cooler were it not for greenhouse gases. This is based on a theoretical calculation based on the Stefan-Boltzmann law of black body radiation. Now the earth is not a black body, but the theoreticians claim they have made the necessary adjustments for this in their calculations. Of course no one can test this by removing supposed greenhouse gases from the atmosphere.

However the moon has no atmosphere. The later Apollo missions left an array of temperature sensors on the moon and recently NASA released an analysis of the results. Amazingly this shows that the moon also has an elevation of temperature (~40K) above that calculated by the theory. Does the moon then have a 'greenhouse' effect? Clearly not as it has no atmosphere. So it looks as if the calculated starting point is wrong and neither the earth nor the moon are kept warmer by any 'greenhouse effect'.

http://climaterealists.com/attachments/database/RadiativeNonEquilbrium_BHermalyn_Final.pdf

Conclusion: there is no such thing as a greenhouse gas.

When a hypothesis in science is contradicted by the observational data *it has been falsified*. If this obvious but fundamental concept is ignored what follows ceases to be science but becomes dangerous self-deception. The IPCC models of climate (based on the erroneous belief that CO_2, as a greenhouse gas, forces climate warming) have been falsified by the observational and experimental data at every level.

The above Appendix draws from the work of Alan Siddons, a radiochemist, Hans Schreuder, an analytical chemist and a member of Mensa, a paper in the International Journal of Modern Physics - *Falsification of the Atmospheric CO_2 Greenhouse Effects within the Frame of Physics*, by Prof. G.Gerlich and Dr R.D. Tscheuschner and *The Greenhouse Effect: Origins, Falsification, and Replacement*, by Timothy Casey B.Sc. (Hons.) Consulting Geologist.

Appendix 2
How the whole world was tricked into believing in Man-made Global Warming

On a day in the summer of 1988 James Hansen (of GISS/NASA), the mentor of Al Gore, gave testimony before a US Senate Hearing that dangerous global warming was almost certainly being caused by human carbon dioxide emissions. The Hearing had been stage-managed by Al Gore. The day had been deliberately chosen as likely to be the hottest day of the year. The night before the Hearing, all the windows had been opened so that the air conditioning would not work properly. Thus everyone was sweating as Hansen made his 'chilling' statements. These dirty tricks were admitted in public on TV in 2007.

This was a complete reversal of the scientific method - announcing a conclusion before observational and experimental work

228

had been conducted. Nonetheless the AGW hypothesis was taken by the Press and politicians to be a fact.

To achieve some semblance of plausibility, it became necessary to adjust what 'evidence' there was to fit the conclusion. This was the purpose of the Intergovernmental Panel on Climate Change, a non-scientific but politically motivated body. And it was through the IPCC that scientists in the UK (at the CRU at UEA) and in the USA (GISS/NOAA) colluded to generate this evidence. The leaked emails make it clear that collusion is the correct word.

To achieve an apparently 'unprecedented' rise in temperature since 1975 a neat trick was used.

Global average temperatures had been calculated using raw data from several thousand weather stations.

In order to show an alarming 'anomaly' (a nearly 1°C rise) they cut the number of weather stations used for raw data by 70-80%, but they kept the full number to calculate the 'starting point' (the significance of this will become clear).

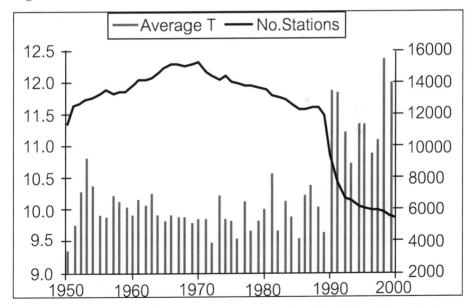

Watts & D'Aleo, *Surface Temperature Records: Policy Driven Deception?*
Published www.scienceandpublicpolicy.org

What they then refused to do was to make the details of this selection available to other scientists. Thus began a long campaign by "The Team" (activist-scientists from CRU and NASA - part of the IPCC machine) to prevent this vital disclosure. Sceptical scientists (no professional scientist can be other than sceptical - *Nullius in Verba*) were suspicious of the secrecy. They were reasonably certain that the modern warming was being exaggerated - but without access to the raw data sources they could not test this.

Only after vigorous efforts using the Freedom of Information Act, which were resisted at every turn by "The Team", using every excuse in the book from 'losing the data' to 'national security' to prevent disclosure, and by the leaking of the emails, has the truth begun to emerge. It is a complicated tale of collusion, deliberate fraud and deceit, but the cull of the weather stations (shown on page 229) crystallizes most clearly how 'The Trick' was performed.

As can be seen, the sudden jump in average temperature (of nearly 1°C) around 1990 'coincided' with the dramatic cull in the number of weather stations - because the ones removed were overwhelmingly the ones in colder regions of the world and in the rural areas (generally cooler than urban areas). Thus, for example, the country of Bolivia (a mountainous country in the Andes region) was airbrushed out to be replaced by an estimated 'average' between the coast of Peru and the Amazon rain forest.

So should we still worry? Is the 'science' still 'robust' as politicians and activists continue to say? The answer is no and no. The 'science' is *bust*, not robust.

A full account of the whole sordid scandal of Climategate can be found in *Climategate: the CRUtape letters* by Steven Mosher and Thomas Fuller, published in the UK by SMP Ltd, 2010 and also in *Hiding the Decline* by Andrew Montford, 2012.

Appendix 3

COMPUTER MODEL PREDICTION
IPCC computer model of atmospheric warming†

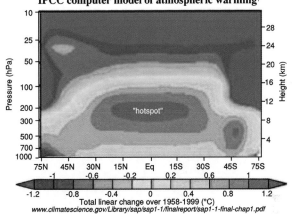

Total linear change over 1958-1999 (°C)
www.climatescience.gov/Library/sap/sap1-1/finalreport/sap1-1-final-chap1.pdf

REALITY
Observed pattern of atmospheric warming†

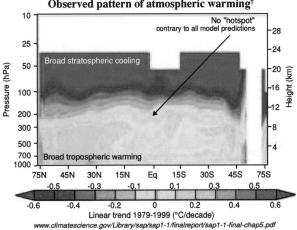

Linear trend 1979-1999 (°C/decade)
www.climatescience.gov/Library/sap/sap1-1/finalreport/sap1-1-final-chap5.pdf

The computer models are essentially two-dimensional 'discs' which attempt to model simplistic ideas and guesswork about the earth's climate. They are, in effect, 'flat-earth' models. They are so bad that when they tried to introduce mountains the air currents passing over them broke the sound barrier!

The CO_2 hypothesis predicts a hot spot above the tropics. As can be seen, reality shows exactly the opposite - a cool spot.

And Finally...

If you really want to worry then worry about this:

HERE COMES THE NEXT ICE AGE!

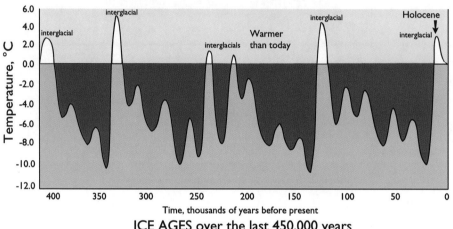

ICE AGES over the last 450,000 years

    If you want to worry then worry about the next big ice age - due quite soon! They last around 80,000 years, interglacials (one of which we are now in) last between 12,000 and 20,000years (maximum).

    Note also that the maximum temperature of each interglacial has been generally decreasing over the last half a million years.

But not this: ocean acidification

Ocean acidification cannot actually happen. Oceans are always slightly alkaline (around pH 8) and are saturated in carbon dioxide. There are even pools of liquid CO_2 in deep ocean trenches. Extra CO_2 dissolves limestone and limestone sediments ($CaCO_3$) to form an alkaline solution of calcium bicarbonate - $Ca(HCO_3)_2$. As Prof. Ian Plimer put it, "Oceans can only become acidic if the earth runs out of rocks."

Bibliography

The inclusion of books in this list does not signify that either I agree with all that they have written or that they would endorse or agree with what I have written.

Archibald, David, *Solar Cycle 24*, Rhaetian Management Pty Ltd 2008

Ager, D. V., *Introducing Geology*, Faber 1961

Andrews, E. H., *God, Science & Evolution*, Evangelical Press 1980

Behe, M. J., *Darwin's Black Box*, The Free Press 1996

Behe, M. J., *The Edge of Evolution*, The Free Press 2008

Berry, R. J., *God and the Biologist*, Apollos 1996

Berry, R. J., ed., *Real Faith, Real Science*, Monarch 1991

Bilello, John C., *Bible and Science*, 2005

Birkett, Kisten, *The essence of Darwinism*, Matthias Media 2001

Booker, C. & R. North, *Scared to Death*, Continuum 2007

Booker, C. *The Real Global Warming Disaster*, Continuum 2009

Calder, Nigel, *The Manic Sun*, Pilkington 1997

Carter, Robert M., *Climate: The Counter Consensus*, Stacey Int. 2010

Chesterton, G. K., *Orthodoxy*, John Lane 1909

Crichton, Michael, *State of Fear*, Harper Collins 2004

Defoe, Daniel, *The Storm*, 1704, re-issued by Penguin 2003

Dreissen, Paul, *Eco-Imperialism: Green Power, Black Death,*
     Merril Press 2003

Ehrenfeld, David, *The Arrogance of Humanism*, OUP 1978

Fruchtenbaum, Arnold, *Messianic Christology*, Ariel Ministries 1998

Gardner, Dan, *Risk*, Virgin Books 2008

Guinness, H. Grattan, *The Approaching End of the Age*, 1879
     [text available on line]

Hartnett, J., *Starlight, Time and the New Physics*, Creation Books 2007

Hayward, Alan, *Creation and Evolution*, SPCK 1994, also SMP Ltd

Hunter, Cornelius G., *Darwin's God*, Brazos Press 2001

Jaki, S. L., *The Saviour of Science*, Scottish Academic Press, 1990

Kaye and Laby, *Table of Physical and Chemical Constants,*
     Longman, 15th Edition

Klaus, Václav, *Blue Planet in Green Shackles,*
     Competitive Enterprise Institute, 2008

Landsberg, Peter T., *Seeking Ultimates,* Institute of Physics
     Publishing 2000

Lawson, Nigel, *An Appeal to Reason*, Duckworth 2008

Lomborg, Bjørn, *the skeptical environmentalist*, CUP 2002

Lomborg, Bjørn, *Cool It*, Marshall Cavendish 2007

Martin, Jobe, *Evolution of a Creationist,* Biblical Discipleship
     Publishers 1994

McGrath, A., *Dawkin's God*, Blackwell 2005

Mellanby, K., *Waste and Pollution,* Harper Collins 1992
Miller, Hugh, *Testimony of the Rocks,* 1856, reprinted SMP Ltd 2001
Monteith, Stanley, *Brotherhood of Darkness*
Monty White, A. J., *What About Origins?,* Dunestone 1978
Morris H., *Scientific Creationism,* 1974
Mosher, Steven & Thomas Fuller, *Climategate: the CRUtape letters,* SMP 2010
Page, Robin, *The Hunting Gene,* Bird's Farm Books 2000
Panek, R., *Seeing and Believing,* Fourth Estate 2001
Plimer, Ian, *Heaven and Earth, global warming: the missing science,*
        Quartet 2009
Polkinghorne, J., *Quarks, Chaos and Christianity,* SPCK 1994
Prasch, James Jacob, *The Final Words of Jesus,* SMP Ltd 1999
Ramm, Bernard, *The Christian View of Science and Scripture,*
        Paternoster Press 1964
Rees, Martin, *Our Final Century,* Arrow Books 2004
Singer, S. F. & D. T. Avery, *Unstoppable Global Warming,*
        Rowman & Littlefield 2007
Spencer, Roy W., *The Great Global Warming Blunder,* Encounter Books 2010
Stoner, P. W., *Science Speaks,* Moody Press 1963
Svensmark, Henrik & Nigel Calder, *The Chilling Stars,* Icon Books 2007
Taverne, Dick, *The March of Unreason,* OUP 2007
Veon, Joan, *The United Nations Global Straitjacket* 1999
Weinberg, Steven, *The First Three Minutes,* Basic Books 1993
Whitcomb, J. and H. Morris, *The Genesis Flood,* 1961
Whitehouse, D., *The Sun; a biography,* Wiley 2006
Wilkinson, D. and R. Frost, *Thinking Clearly about God and Science,*
        Monarch, Evangelical Alliance 1996
Williams, Austin, *The Enemies of Progress,* Imprint Academic 2008
Wonderly, Dan, *God's Time-Records in Ancient Sediments,* 1977
Young, Davis A., *Creation and the Flood,* Baker 1977
DVD: *The Great Global Warming Swindle*, Martin Durkin,
        WagTV for Channel 4 2007
Websites:
www.copenhagenclimatechallenge.org
www.climaterealists.com
www.globalwarmingheartland.org
www.nzclimatescience.net
www.wattsupwiththat.com
www.ilovemycarbondioxide.com
www.weatheraction.com
http://video.google.com/videoplay?docid=2009981932959450626&hl=en
(a video of the author explaining 'Global Warming')

Glossary

Amino acids: organic chemicals with acid and amine attachments. There are twenty specific amino acid 'bricks' that make up all proteins in living things.

Black holes: At first these were only inferred to exist theoretically. The Law of Gravity (p.17) suggests that when a supernova collapses into a neutron star, in some cases, where the neutron star is very massive (usually reckoned as about twice the mass of our sun), it could go on collapsing further still. As the force of gravity operates under an inverse square law, as the distance between objects decreases, the force rapidly increases. If two objects actually coalesce then the distance between them becomes virtually zero and the force of gravity therefore becomes virtually infinite—the extreme instance of which is called a Singularity.

In these circumstances a black hole might form where the gravitational field is so extreme that no light can escape from it. Therefore their existence can only be inferred from the behaviour of visible stars near such a hole. There is recent evidence that the centre of the Milky Way (and every galaxy) contains a massive black hole (a million times as dense as our sun).

Enzyme: a protein designed to catalyse biochemical reactions in a living cell.

Gamma rays: very high energy electromagnetic radiation of higher frequency than X-rays. The EM spectrum: Gamma rays, X-rays, ultraviolet rays, light, heat, microwave and radio.

Half-life: radioactive elements (such as Carbon-14) decay into non-radioactive products exponentially: some faster some slower: as an exponential decay never strictly speaking finishes (it is always halving), the rate is best noted as the time taken for the radioactive element to decay to half its original concentration.

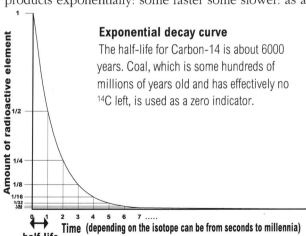

Exponential decay curve
The half-life for Carbon-14 is about 6000 years. Coal, which is some hundreds of millions of years old and has effectively no ^{14}C left, is used as a zero indicator.

Amount of radioactive element

1
1/2
1/4
1/8
1/16
1/32

0 1 2 3 4 5 6 7 .....
half-life

Time (depending on the isotope can be from seconds to millennia)

Howard Hughes syndrome: Howard Hughes was an entrepreneur and aircraft manufacturer in the USA during the 1930s and 1940s. His personal life became increasingly neurotic and bizarre. He suffered from extreme hypochondria—eventually fearing any human contact, lest he become infected. His last days were spent in expensive isolation in a penthouse in York St., Houston, Texas!

LXX or Septuagint: a version of the Old Testament translated from the original Hebrew into Greek around the 1st-2nd century BC. Tradition has it that 70 scholars in separate rooms all produced an identical translation.

Midrash: best explained in *The Final Words of Jesus* by Jacob Prasch; see bibliography.

Lysenko, Trophimo: a Russian peasant who believed himself a great scientist and geneticist. He claimed seeds could be 'vernalised' so that they would grow in the tundra of Siberia. Because his ideas conflicted with the West's 'decadent' science, Stalin saw him as a great asset to the regime. He became a very powerful figure and was ruthless towards any who doubted his ideas; many of whom ended up either dead or in the gulags. The actual results of his agricultural madness were starvation and death on a massive scale.

Malaria: a mosquito-borne parasite infecting the blood, causing fever and quite often death if untreated.

NGO (non-Governmental Organisation): usually a development agency or charity. Many go along with politically correct views on Climate Change because they want to keep the ear of governments.

Phanerozoic: the 'Appearance of Life', the time in the earth's pre-history from which fossils can be found.

Plasma: this is regarded as a fourth state of matter distinct from solid, liquid or gas. Plasma is a fluid state of atoms where electrons are freed from their atomic nuclei by the temperature or electric or magnetic force fields. Atoms of hydrogen or helium lose all their electrons and become protons (hydrogen) or alpha particles (helium). Heavier atoms lose only some of their electrons. At high temperatures and pressures the charged nuclei can smash together despite the electric forces pushing them apart. This can lead to nuclear fusion. See page 33 for more details.

Succession: the term given to describe progression of life forms from the Phanerozoic Period from 'simple' creatures to humans.

Index of Bible verses

Index

You can purchase this book or others directly from
St. Matthew Publishing Ltd
1 Barnfield, Common Lane, Hemingford Abbots
Huntingdon PE28 9AX   UK
01480 399098
Email: PF.SMP@dial.pipex.com
www.stmatthewpublishing.co.uk
or order through your local bookshop.
Please email, telephone or write for a catalogue
or to make an order.

A selection of publications available:

Books:

Climategate: the CRUtape Letters, Mosher & Fuller 2010
The Testimony of the Rocks, Hugh Miller 1856, 2001
Creation & Evolution, Alan Hayward 1985, 2006
Beware the New Prophets, Bill Randles 1999
Final Words of Jesus, James Jacob Prasch 1999
Israel, the Church and the Jews, James Jacob Prasch 2008
Alpha: the Unofficial Guide, Overview, Elizabeth McDonald 2001
Rome, Babylon the Great and Europe, Bob Mitchell 2003
Darwin's God, Cornelius Hunter, Brazos Press 2001
An Appeal to Reason, Nigel Lawson, Duckworth 2008
Unstoppable Global Warming, S. F. Singer & D. T. Avery,
        Rowman & Littlefield 2007
The Chilling Stars, Henrik Svensmark & Nigel Calder,
        Icon Books 2007

Booklets:

101 reasons for leaving the EU 2002
Reliability of the New Testament, Philip Foster 2005

DVDs:

The Great Global Warming Swindle, Durkin, WagTV 2007